Revise KS3

Science

Bob McDuell

Contents

Yes.

Science at Key Stage 3

Introduction to Key Stage 3 Science

Key Stage 3 is an important part of your progress in Science. At Key Stage 2 you will have had a range of experiences in Science and will have learnt some important scientific words and principles. At the end of Year 6 you will have had your progress assessed.

You will start the GCSE Science courses after Key Stage 3. As there are no formal Key Stage 3 exams at the end of Year 9, different schools now start GCSE courses at different times. Many still start them in Year 10, as was always the case. Some now, however, start these courses either at the start of Year 9 or at some time during Year 9.

Depending upon the school, you may be taught Key Stage 3 Science in Science lessons or you may be taught Science with other subjects in an integrated programme. Whatever approach your school uses, Key Stage 3 is important as a preparation for the GCSE courses. It is important to master the ideas within this book to ensure that your GCSE development is not impaired.

Successful study

This study guide should be used to help you throughout Key Stage 3 to make sure you know and understand the key facts and issues as you go along. You should then be able to use this information to help you answer questions.

Success in school depends on regular planned work over a period of time rather than panic bursts of very hard work just before an examination.

If you develop the habit of regularly reviewing the work you have done in school, and making sure you understand it, it is less likely to cause you problems when you study similar areas in GCSE.

Remember, schools approach the content in different orders. When you have studied a topic in class, find the relevant topic in this revision guide.

You can find more information on www.qca.org.uk/curriculum.

Assessment

Throughout Key Stage 3 you will have assessments in Science. These assessments enable both you and your teacher to see how much progress you have made. At the end of Key Stage 3, your teacher will need to decide what National Curriculum level you are working at.

During Key Stage 3, your teacher will follow a structured approach to pupil assessment in Science. This is referred to as APP (Assessing Pupils' Progress) and it means your teacher can:
- track your progress in Science
- use diagnostic information about your strengths and weaknesses
- assign you an overall National Curriculum level for Science at the end of Key Stage 3.

Attainment targets

Science at Key Stage 3 is split into four Attainment Targets. In this book it is divided into 5 chapters.

Chapter 1 – Attainment target 1: How science works

How Science Works is an important aspect of Science, which is about how scientists use a systematic approach in tackling a scientific problem. You will carry out practical activities to support your development in this attainment task.

Although the content for How Science Works appears at the beginning of this book in Chapter 1, you should understand that it may overlap with the content of the other attainment targets because it is also about the application and implication of science, e.g. ethics.

Chapter 2 – Attainment target 2: Organisms, their behaviour and the environment

Organisms, their behaviour and the environment is the area of Science called Biology. This content is found in Chapter 2 with some aspects of the Environment in Chapter 5.

You will study how the human body works, how plants work, how living things are grouped and how species can change from generation to generation. You will study aspects of the environment including depletion of the ozone layer and global warming.

Chapter 3 – Attainment target 3: Materials, their properties and the Earth

Materials, their properties and the Earth is the area of Science called Chemistry. It includes classifying materials in different ways, changing properties (including chemical reactions) and grouping materials according to their properties.

This attainment target also includes content on rocks (Chapter 5). This area of science is called Geology.

Chapter 4 – Attainment target 4: Energy, forces and space

Energy, forces and space is the area of Science called Physics. It includes electricity, sound, light, forces and motion, energy resources and energy transfer.

This attainment target also includes a study of the Solar System (Chapter 5).

Chapter 5 – Aspects of attainment targets 2–4

The content in Chapter 5 (The Environment, Earth and Universe) is material that might be taught in conjunction with other departments, e.g. Geography.

Science at Key Stage 3

Features in this Study Guide

Key Point boxes highlight important things you must remember, e.g. formulae and definitions.

Margin comments contain invaluable advice from examiners.

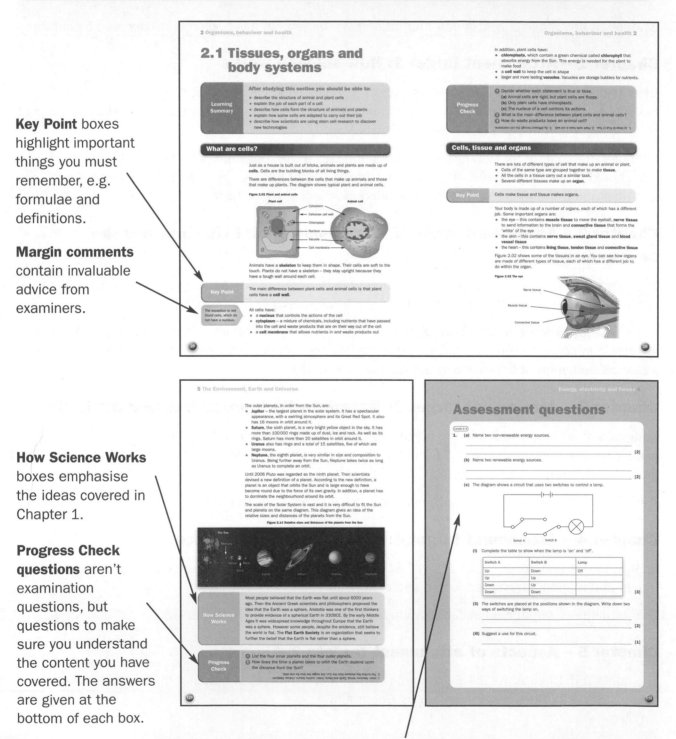

How Science Works boxes emphasise the ideas covered in Chapter 1.

Progress Check questions aren't examination questions, but questions to make sure you understand the content you have covered. The answers are given at the bottom of each box.

Assessment questions (found at the end of each chapter) are questions designed to give you an idea about the level you are working at. There are questions at Levels 3–4, Levels 5–6 and Levels 7–8. The answers to these questions are found on pages 139–141. By checking your answers and looking at what you have got right or wrong, you should be able to gain an idea of the level you are working at.

1 How science works

Chapter One		Studied	Revised	Assessment questions
1.1 Investigations	– Scientific method			
1.2 Planning	– Investigations			
1.3 Risks and hazards	– Risk assessments			
1.4 Selecting apparatus	– Selecting apparatus			
1.5 Recording results	– Using tables for results			
1.6 Displaying results	– Bar charts – Line graphs			
1.7 Drawing and explaining conclusions	– Using data to draw conclusions			
1.8 Evaluation	– Evaluating an experiment			

1.1 Investigations

<table>
<tr>
<td>Learning Summary</td>
<td>After studying this section you should be able to:
<ul>
<li>describe the stages in a scientific investigation</li>
<li>distinguish dependent and independent variables</li>
</ul>
</td>
</tr>
</table>

Scientific method

Scientists solve problems by carrying out **investigations**. In an investigation a scientist uses information to help set up the investigation.

Planning an investigation is not a haphazard process. It has to be planned carefully or it will be useless. During Key Stage 3 you will tackle problems and use investigations to solve them.

Scientists have a scientific procedure or **scientific method** they use to get from a problem they wish to solve to an answer.

If you have a scientific problem to solve, there is a set procedure you should follow:

1. First make sure you have the problem in a proper form to study. Do not make your investigation too wide. Check that the answer cannot just be looked up in a book or on the Internet. For example, 'what causes iron to rust?' is a question readily answered in a textbook or on the Internet.

2. Think about the question and think about a possible answer based upon what you know from similar situations or from research. We call this a **hypothesis**. Write down your hypothesis and briefly write your thinking that led you to make it. From your hypothesis, make **predictions** that you can test by experiment.

3. Now plan experiments to test your hypothesis. It is important to do your plan carefully. In your experiments there are things that might change, which are called **variables**. Variables can be divided into two types:
   - **Independent variable** – this is one that you can change.
   - **Dependent variable** – this is one that you cannot change.

For example, if you are investigating how fast a chemical reaction can take place, you could carry out the reaction at different temperatures or with different concentrations of reactants. You choose the temperature and concentration used, so these are the independent variables. The time for the reaction is a dependent variable because it depends upon the temperature and concentrations you have chosen.

It is often important to carry out an experiment where all the independent variables are kept constant. This is called a **control experiment**.

You should only change one independent variable at a time. This is to ensure that it is a **fair test** (you should know about fair tests from Key Stage 2). If you change both temperature and concentration at the same time you cannot tell what effect each one has. Decide what results you are going to take and how to record them.

4. Now carry out the experiments correctly. Where possible you should repeat results to make sure you get similar answers. Record these results carefully and include all results even if they seem to spoil your ideas.

5. Look at your results and your hypothesis. Do they match? If they do not match, revise your hypothesis and then carry out further experiments.

6. If they do match completely, you have produced a **theory**. A theory is an idea that has experimental support. At this point other scientists might attempt to check your results by carrying out similar experiments. Only when all scientists agree can we say you have produced a scientific truth or a **law** or a **principle**.

All of these stages can be summarised in a scientific method cycle (see Figure 1.01).

Figure 1.01 Scientific method cycle

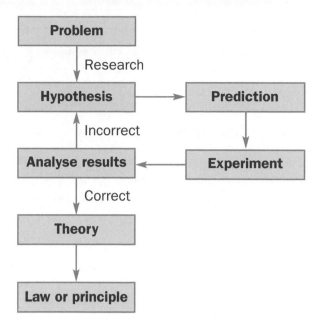

1.2 Planning

Investigations

During Key Stage 3 you might be expected to conduct some planning. You may then have the opportunity to try out your plan and, if necessary after looking at the results, modify it.

When devising a plan, make sure you are only changing one variable at a time, while keeping all of the others the same.

For example, how fast a chemical reaction can take place depends upon different things, e.g. the concentration of the reacting substances (reactants), the temperature, and whether the solids are lumpy or powdery. If you want to investigate the effects of changing temperature on a chemical reaction, you must carry out a series of reactions at a range of different temperatures, keeping the other independent variables (concentrations and how powdered the solids are) the same.

Before doing your planning you might carry out some research.

The research might be using a **primary source** of information, i.e. an experiment. You could try out the experiment at room temperature with a given set of concentrations and powered solids. If the reaction is too fast, this might suggest you use lower concentrations.

You might also look up information in a **secondary source**, i.e. a book or the Internet. This might give you ideas from similar investigations that other people have carried out. It is important to make a note of any secondary sources you have used.

You must also decide how much data you need to collect. Remember, once you have completed the experiment you probably will not be able to go back and collect more data. Aim to collect more data than you think you will need.

Some investigations, particularly biological ones, are very complex and it is difficult to identify all of the possible variables. If the variables cannot be identified then they cannot be controlled. This may lead to some misleading conclusions.

Example

Some students carry out an investigation to compare the speed of different students running over 100m.

Three students have stopwatches and are the timekeepers. Three other students are running, and the timekeepers time each of these students in turn as they run 100m. The results are shown in the table below.

Student running	Time to run 100m (seconds)			Average (seconds)
	Timekeeper 1	Timekeeper 2	Timekeeper 3	
Adey	15.0	14.9	14.9	14.9
Brian	16.5	15.5	15.3	15.4
Chris	16.6	16.0	16.9	

The results for Adey are all close together and therefore are **reliable**. It is easy to work out the average. The calculator reads 14.9333333333 seconds, but we should record the average to the same number of decimal places as the timings, so this is 14.9s.

With Brian's results, two of the results are close together and it looks as though Timekeeper 1 has made a mistake. We can calculate the average without using Timekeeper 1's results.

The three results for Chris are very different and it seems meaningless to calculate an average. It would probably be better to get Chris to run the 100m again.

1.3 Risks and hazards

Learning Summary

After studying this section you should be able to:

- identify hazards in a practical situation
- suggest ways of controlling risks and hazards
- recall the common hazard signs

Risk assessments

You must always carry out experiments carefully, and follow the instructions your teacher gives you. You may have to take special precautions.

Teachers have to prepare a **risk assessment** before carrying out experiments. This identifies the hazards and what should be done to ensure that the experiment is carried out safely.

For example:
- Experiments that give off irritating or poisonous gases should be carried out in a fume cupboard. If there is no fume cupboard, the experiment might be carried out outside.
- For experiments in which liquid splashes or sparks are expected, protective goggles should be worn.
- Care must be taken when using micro-organisms or live tissue in experiments, or certain types of radiation.
- Some chemicals are particularly hazardous and their hazardous nature is clearly indicated on the container by standard hazard symbols. Handle these chemicals carefully.

Figure 1.02 explains about some of the safety/hazard symbols. You might see these symbols on bottles of chemicals in your school laboratory and also on household products such as aerosol canisters and bottles of household bleach.

Figure 1.02 Common chemical safety/hazard symbols

Symbol	Hazard	Description of hazard
	Explosive	Chemicals that explode
	Oxidising	Chemicals that react exothermically with other chemicals
	Highly flammable	Chemicals that may catch fire in contact with air, only need brief contact with an ignition source
	Toxic	Chemicals that at very low levels cause damage to health and possible death
	Harmful	Chemicals that may cause damage to health
	Corrosive	Chemicals that may destroy living tissue on contact
	Irritant	Chemicals that may cause inflammation to the skin or other mucous membranes
	Dangerous for the environment	Chemicals that may present an immediate or delayed danger to one or more components of the environment

Road tankers that transport chemicals will have a safety label on the side or back of the tanker.

This label shows everybody what is being carried in the tanker. In the event of an accident and the contents spilling onto the roadway, the emergency services can tell from the code how the spillage should be safely treated.

Figure 1.03 Hazard sign on a road tanker

iStockphoto / Thinkstock

When working in the school laboratory or when scientists are working in an industrial laboratory, care must be taken to identify risks and plans must be made to avoid injuries.

Figure 1.04A shows some students working in a school laboratory and Figure 1.04B lists some of the risks and what should be done to control them. You may be able to see other risks.

Figure 1.04A Students working in a school laboratory

Figure 1.04B Risks and how to control them

Risk	How to control risk
Fire exit doorway obstructed	Remove boxes
Cupboard door and drawer open	Close them
Poison cupboard open	Close and lock
Concentrated acid on high shelf	Take down from the shelf and lock away
Curtains close to lit Bunsen burner	Remove burner from current position. Replace curtains with a blind
Spilt liquid on the floor may cause somebody to slip	Mop up the liquid
Fire extinguisher missing	Replace the fire extinguisher
Girl picking up large bottle by its neck	Bottle should be supported underneath with the other hand
Thermometer close to edge of the bench where it may roll off	Move the thermometer to a safer place
Tripod near to the edge of the bench	Push it further onto the bench
Food in the laboratory	Remove the food from the laboratory
Broken apparatus on the bench	Clear up to avoid cuts

Laboratories can be dangerous places, but sensible consideration of hazards and risks avoids most accidents.

1.4 Selecting apparatus

Learning Summary

After studying this section you should be able to:
- choose suitable equipment to ensure precision

Selecting apparatus

In school there are limited opportunities for you to select equipment. The equipment you use is often the equipment your teacher provides. This in turn may depend on the equipment available.

One of the important things you have to do is to select the most suitable piece of apparatus to use to do a measurement.

If you are measuring length you could use a...
- micrometer
- 30cm ruler
- metre rule
- steel tape 20m long
- trundle wheel
- odometer in a car's speedometer.

A trundle wheel is a wheel with a handle. As you push it along there is a clicking sound every metre. So if you count the clicks it gives you the distance.

Which piece of apparatus you use depends upon the job you have to do. For example:
- If you are measuring the length of a pencil, a 30cm ruler would be best.
- If you were measuring the distance between Nelson's Column in London and Stonehenge in Wiltshire a ruler would not be very suitable. The odometer is probably best.

Figure 1.05 shows four pieces of Science apparatus that could be used to measure 25cm³ of water.

Figure 1.05

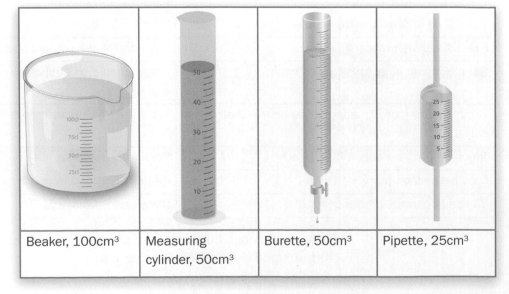

| Beaker, 100cm³ | Measuring cylinder, 50cm³ | Burette, 50cm³ | Pipette, 25cm³ |

The most appropriate measuring instrument depends on how precise the measurement of water needs to be.

If **approximately** 25cm^3 of water is needed (and the water measurement could therefore be between 20–30cm^3 of water) then the beaker with its approximate gradations would be suitable.

If it is important that the volume actually measured is between perhaps 24cm^3 and 26cm^3, then the measuring cylinder would be suitable.

For greater **precision** either the burette or the pipette should be used. The pipette is made to deliver exactly 25.0cm^3 every time. The burette can be used to measure any volume up to 50.0cm^3. The pipette and burette are **precise**.

Example

Amy tries to measure out four samples of 25cm^3 of water using four different measuring instruments in turn. After each measurement she adds the water to a weighed beaker and finds the mass of water she has measured out. Amy knows that 1.0cm^3 of water has a mass of 1.0g, so she can then work out the volume of water measured.

Her results are shown below.

Apparatus used	Mass of water (grams)		
	1	2	3
Beaker	22.3	28.6	21.0
Measuring cylinder	25.4	24.6	25.1
Burette	25.1	25.2	24.8
Pipette	25.0	25.0	25.1

You will notice that the readings for the burette and the pipette are much closer to 25.0cm^3 than the beaker or measuring cylinder. This is what you should expect.

Sometimes when you are carrying out investigations you should consider taking repeat readings and then calculating an average. The average you obtain should be more **reliable** than any individual result. If any result(s) is very different from the others, you would be wise to ignore this one and average the others.

If you are measuring the length and breadth of this book, repeat readings are not necessary. The distances are fixed and will not change.

In your school laboratory your teacher will usually tell you what method you should use. However, there may be opportunities for you to adapt the method. You should always check with your teacher before you make any changes.

Progress Check

1. There are five pieces of apparatus.
   Ammeter   Ruler   Spring balance   Stopwatch   Thermometer
   Which piece of apparatus would you use to measure the following?
   (a) mass **(b)** length **(c)** time **(d)** temperature **(e)** electric current
2. What would be the best piece of equipment to measure the following?
   (a) the length of a football pitch **(b)** the thickness of a wire

2. (a) Trundle wheel (b) Micrometer
1. (a) Spring balance (b) Ruler (c) Stopwatch (d) Thermometer (e) Ammeter

1.5 Recording results

Learning Summary

After studying this section you should be able to:

- record observations and measurements in a suitable table.

Using tables for results

It is important to write down the observations or results of experiments as soon as you collect them. This is so they are not forgotten. The results or observations are usually best displayed in a table.

Often it is better to design and draw up the table before you start collecting the results or observations.

Figure 1.06 shows a table of results for an experiment where zinc oxide and copper sulfate crystals are heated. Observations about the state of the crystals are taken in three states:

1. Before heating

2. When they are hot

3. After they cool down again.

When recording colours, try to say more than just 'blue' or 'yellow'. There are many shades of blue and yellow.

Figure 1.06

Substance	Observations		
	Before heating	On heating	On cooling
zinc oxide	white powder	pale yellow powder	white powder
copper sulfate crystals	pale blue crystals	white powder and steam	white powder

Figure 1.07 shows a table of results for an experiment to measure the temperature of water being heated in a beaker using a Bunsen burner. The results are collected every 15 seconds.

Figure 1.07

Time (seconds)	0	15	30	45	60	75
Temperature (°C)	20	28	36	44	52	60

1.6 Displaying results

Learning Summary

After studying this section you should be able to:

- display results in a bar chart
- display results in a line graph
- draw suitable lines of best fit
- identify anomalous results

Bar charts

A **bar chart** is a diagram that shows the numerical values of the different variables. These numerical values are represented by the height or length of lines or rectangles of equal width. The bars or lines can be drawn vertically or horizontally.

Figures 1.08A and B shows two bar charts, which show the number of cars sold in different colours. Figure 1.08A has vertical bars and Figure 1.08B has horizontal bars.

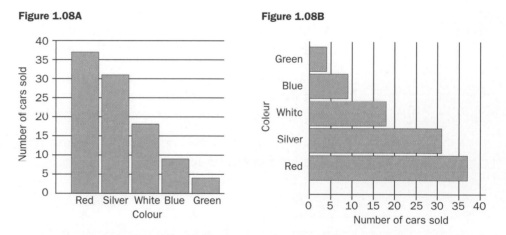

Figure 1.08A

Figure 1.08B

A bar chart is a good way of representing data where there is no mathematical relationship between the two sets of data. If there is a mathematical relationship, a **line graph** is better.

Line graphs

Figure 1.07 shows scientific data that can be drawn as a line graph.

The independent variable (the one you can choose, i.e. time) goes along the horizontal axis (*x*-axis). The dependent variable (the one you measure, i.e. temperature) goes on the vertical axis (*y*-axis).

Draw the axes on the graph and choose suitable scales so the graph fills at least half the piece of graph paper. Plot the points carefully.

Figure 1.09 shows the line graph for the data in Figure 1.07

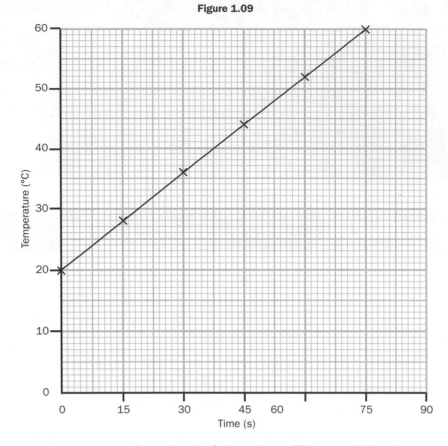

Figure 1.09

A straight line passes through all of the points. This graph line does not go through the origin (i.e. the point 0,0) as many students might expect.

The best line you can draw though the plotted points is called the **line of best fit**. In the graph above all of the points are on this line, but this is not always the case. The line of best fit may be a straight line or a curved line.

Figure 1.10 shows the line graph for the extension of a spring when different forces are applied.

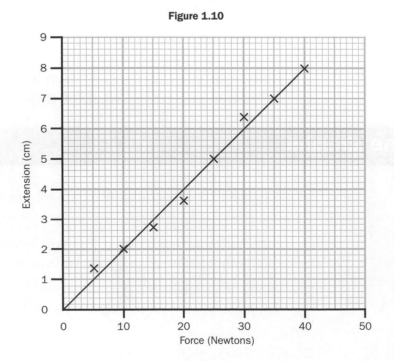

Figure 1.10

You should not draw a dot-to-dot line but a line of best fit – in this case a straight line. The points that are off the line are **anomalous points**. They occur because for some reason you have not got the expected result. When drawing the line of best fit, the number of anomalous points above and below the line should be the same.

During Key Stage 3 you may get the opportunity to use a data logger to collect results of an experiment. The data logger is a type of computer that can be fitted with different probes, e.g. temperature, oxygen concentration, etc. The results of the data logger experiment will be printed out as a graph.

1.7 Drawing and explaining conclusions

Learning Summary	**After studying this section you should be able to:** • identify appropriate trends or patterns in results

Using data to draw conclusions

Having drawn a line graph you should look for any **trends** or patterns in the data.

Looking at the graph in Figure 1.09, students often write that there is a positive correlation, but this does not adequately explain what is happening in the graph; you should write that as time increases temperature increases. The line of best fit does not go though the origin, so there is nothing more that you can comment on from the graph.

In Figure 1.10 you could write that as the force increases, the extension increases. In this graph the line of best fit does go through the origin, so you can write that the extension is directly proportional to the force.

It is important to relate the results to the corresponding Science. You will find examples of this throughout this book.

Progress Check

① Three sketch graphs **(a)–(c)** are shown below. For each graph, describe as completely as you can the trends shown by the graph.

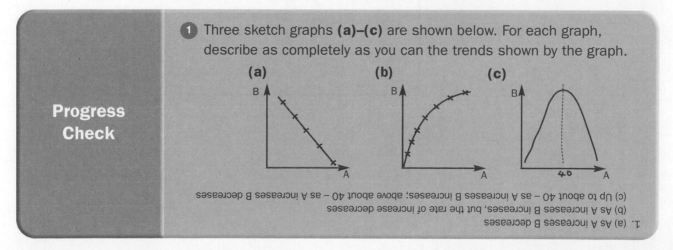

1. (a) As A increases B decreases
(b) As A increases B increases, but the rate of increase decreases
(c) Up to about 40 – as A increases B increases; above about 40 – as A increases B decreases

1.8 Evaluation

Learning Summary

After studying this section you should be able to:

- identify possible errors in methods and suggest improvements
- decide whether the data is sufficient to support a conclusion

Evaluating an experiment

When carrying out an investigation it is important to look critically at the method used, its faults and how it could be improved. Also it is important to consider carefully the data collected.

- Was sufficient data collected?
- Was it the right data?
- Does the data support any prediction or scientific knowledge?
- Was the data reliable?

This process is called **evaluation**.

You will find examples through this book where there are experiments that could be improved.

Figure 1.11 shows the graph of results of an experiment.

Figure 1.11 Results graph

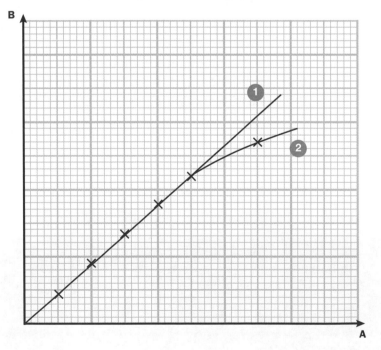

Looking at the first six points on the graph could lead to the conclusion that A is directly proportional to B, i.e. there is a straight line through the origin.

However, what about the last point?
- Is it an anomalous result with the graph continuing in a straight line **1**?

or

- Is the graph levelling off **2**?

To be sure you would need to take further results beyond the sixth point.

When you get data from a secondary source, e.g. the Internet or a computer simulation, you cannot be sure how these results were obtained.

Progress Check

1 Suggest two ways that you can conclude that results are reliable.

1. If there are repeats; If the values are close together; If the points are all very close to the line of best fit.

Assessment questions

Note: How Science Works questions refer to content from different parts of the course. Each question here is referenced to a relevant page in this book.

Levels 3–4

Reference p19

1. The graph below shows how the number of cigarettes smoked per day changes the risk of a person dying from lung cancer.

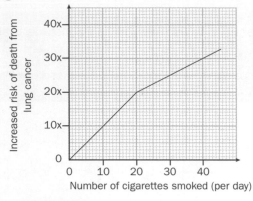

How does the risk of lung cancer change if a person increases their smoking from 10-a-day to 20-a-day?

_____

_____ **[2]**

Reference p17 and 19

2. The table below shows the animals collected at two different locations.
    Site A: A damp shady area of the garden.
    Site B: A dry open area of grass with a shaded position.

Animal	Number of animals found at location	
	A	B
Snails	55	1
Worms	20	5
Centipedes	5	2
Ants	40	25
Spiders	20	15
Beetles	20	10
Aphids	20	40

(a) What is the big difference in conditions at the two locations?

_____

_____ **[1]**

Assessment questions

(b) Which animal was found in larger numbers at site B rather than site A?

_____ **[1]**

(c) Finish the pie chart showing the distribution of the animals at site A. Each segment is 20°.

[2]

(d) Which animal is likely to be the secondary consumer? Give a reason for your answer.

_____

_____ **[2]**

Levels 5–6

Reference p17–18

3. The span of a hand is the distance between the tip of the thumb and the tip of the little finger when the hand is stretched out. The table shows the hand span measurements of 30 pupils.

Range of span (cm)	Number of pupils
10.0–11.4	2
11.5–12.9	6
13.0–14.4	11
14.5–15.9	8
16.0–17.4	3

(a) Explain whether hand span is an example of continuous or discontinuous variation.

_____

_____ **[1]**

(b) Plot the results on a bar chart.

[2]

Assessment questions

(c) Describe the pattern of variation these results show.

_____

_____

_____ **[3]**

(d) A glove maker might find these results useful when planning how many pairs of gloves to produce in each size.
Do these results provide sufficient evidence? Explain your answer.

_____

_____

_____

_____

_____ **[3]**

4. This question is about germination of seeds.

Reference p8–10, 19

The diagram shows an experiment where pea seeds are germinated. The peas in experiment B were boiled before being used, but the ones in experiment A were not. Room temperature is 20°C experiment.

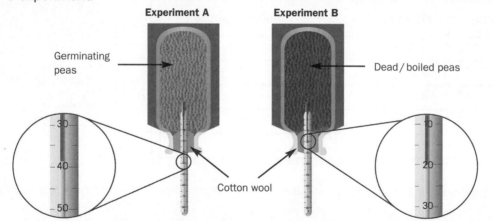

(a) Explain what the results in experiment A show.

_____

_____

_____

_____ **[2]**

(b) Experiment B is a control experiment. Why is this experiment necessary?

_____

_____ **[1]**

Assessment questions

(Levels 7–8)

5. **Reference p20–21. Refer back to Q1.**

A scientist claims that doubling the number of cigarettes smoked each day doubles the risk of lung cancer. Discuss this claim.

_____

_____

_____ **[3]**

6. **Reference p16–18, 20**

Five groups of students carried out an experiment. They burnt different masses of magnesium ribbon in air. Each group found the mass of magnesium oxide produced. Their results are summarised in the table.

Group	Mass of magnesium (g)	Mass of magnesium oxide (g)	Mass of oxygen combined (g)
A	0.90	1.50	0.60
B	1.20	2.00	i)
C	1.50	2.50	ii)
D	1.80	2.70	iii)
E	2.10	3.50	iv)

(a) Complete the table of results. **[1]**

(b) Plot the results on the grid. Plot the mass of oxygen on the *x*-axis against the mass of magnesium on the *y*-axis. Draw the line of best fit through the points. **[3]**

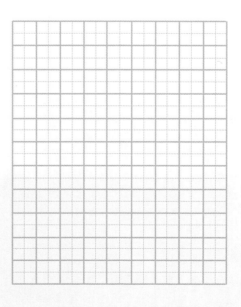

Assessment questions

(c) One group produced unexpected results. Which group was this? How do you know? Suggest what might have gone wrong with their experiment if all the weighings were correct.

_____

_____

_____

_____

_____ **[3]**

(d) Another group tried to carry out the experiment with 0.2g of magnesium. Suggest why it is difficult for them to get accurate results.

_____

_____

_____ **[1]**

(e) The line of best fit goes through the origin (0,0). Why can this be justified?

_____

_____ **[1]**

2 Organisms, behaviour and health

			Studied	Revised	Assessment Questions
2.1	Tissues, organs and body systems	– What are cells? – Cells, tissue and organs – Specialised cells – Stem cells			
2.2	Human reproduction	– Adolescence – Menstruation – Fertilisation – The developing foetus			
2.3	Diet, drugs and disease	– Food and diet – Vitamins – Mineral salts – Breathing – Effects of smoking – Effects of alcohol – Effects of drugs – Microbes and disease – How the body prevents micro-organisms entering – Sexually transmitted infections			
2.4	Classification	– Classification of animals – Classification of plants			
2.5	Variation	– Variation – Nature or nurture – Mutations – Selective breeding – Genetic engineering			
2.6	Behaviour	– Types of behaviour – Investigating behaviour			
2.7	Environment and feeding relationships	– Habitats – How plants and animals are adapted – Feeding – Changes in the environment			
2.8	Respiration and photosynthesis	– Respiration in human cells – What is the role of the lungs? – Photosynthesis			

2.1 Tissues, organs and body systems

	After studying this section you should be able to:
Learning Summary	<ul><li>describe the structure of animal and plant cells</li><li>explain the job of each part of a cell</li><li>describe how cells form the structure of animals and plants</li><li>explain how some cells are adapted to carry out their job</li><li>describe how scientists are using stem cell research to discover new technologies</li></ul>

What are cells?

Just as a house is built out of bricks, animals and plants are made up of **cells**. Cells are the building blocks of all living things.

There are differences between the cells that make up animals and those that make up plants. The diagram shows typical plant and animal cells.

Figure 2.01 Plant and animal cells

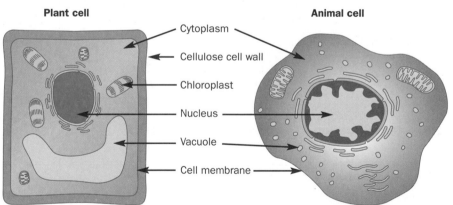

Animals have a **skeleton** to keep them in shape. Their cells are soft to the touch. Plants do not have a skeleton – they stay upright because they have a tough wall around each cell.

Key Point	The main difference between plant cells and animal cells is that plant cells have a **cell wall**.

The exception is red blood cells, which do not have a nucleus.

All cells have:
- a **nucleus** that controls the actions of the cell
- **cytoplasm** – a mixture of chemicals, including nutrients that have passed into the cell and waste products that are on their way out of the cell
- a **cell membrane** that allows nutrients in and waste products out

In addition, plant cells have:
- **chloroplasts**, which contain a green chemical called **chlorophyll** that absorbs energy from the Sun. This energy is needed for the plant to make food
- a **cell wall** to keep the cell in shape
- larger and more lasting **vacuoles**. Vacuoles are storage bubbles for nutrients.

Progress Check

1 Decide whether each statement is true or false.
   (a) Animal cells are rigid, but plant cells are floppy.
   (b) Only plant cells have chloroplasts.
   (c) The nucleus of a cell controls its actions.
2 What is the main difference between plant cells and animal cells?
3 How do waste products leave an animal cell?

1. a) False b) True c) True 2. Plant cells have a cell wall. 3. By diffusion through the cell membrane.

Cells, tissue and organs

There are lots of different types of cell that make up an animal or plant.
- Cells of the same type are grouped together to make **tissue**.
- All the cells in a tissue carry out a similar task.
- Several different tissues make up an **organ**.

Key Point

Cells make tissue and tissue makes organs.

Your body is made up of a number of organs, each of which has a different job. Some important organs are:
- the eye – this contains **muscle tissue** to move the eyeball, **nerve tissue** to send information to the brain and **connective tissue** that forms the 'white' of the eye
- the skin – this contains **nerve tissue**, **sweat gland tissue** and **blood vessel tissue**
- the heart – this contains **lining tissue**, **tendon tissue** and **connective tissue**

Figure 2.02 shows some of the tissues in an eye. You can see how organs are made of different types of tissue, each of which has a different job to do within the organ.

Figure 2.02 The eye

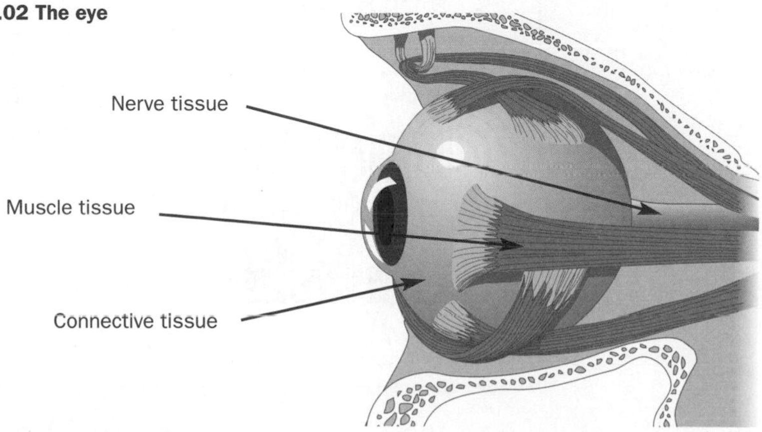

Nerve tissue

Muscle tissue

Connective tissue

Specialised cells

Questions about ways in which cells are adapted to do their job are common in tests and examinations.

Cells in different tissues have different jobs to do. Their shape is adapted so that they can do their job efficiently.

The diagrams show some specialised cells and how they are adapted to do a certain job.

Leaf cell Chloroplast	This cell from the **upper** surface of a leaf has lots of chloroplasts to absorb energy from the Sun. Cells in the underneath part of a leaf have very few chloroplasts.
Root hair cell	This **root hair** cell has no chloroplasts – it is underground. It has a large surface area so that water and minerals can pass into the cell. The job of root hairs is to absorb substances from the soil.
Sperm cell Nucleus	A **sperm** cell is a male sex cell. It needs to travel a long way so it has a tail to propel it and a streamlined shape.
Egg cell Cytoplasm Nucleus	An **egg** cell (ovum) is a female sex cell. It is much bigger than a sperm. It does not have to propel itself and it only moves slowly. A hen's egg is much larger than a human egg because it also contains the food needed for the fertilised egg to grow.
Cells with cilia	Cells in the **trachea** or **windpipe** have tiny hairs called **cilia**. The job of these hairs is to trap bacteria and dust so they do not enter the lungs.

Stem cells

Stem cells are cells found in most organisms. They are able to grow into different specialised cell types.

In humans, stem cells may be obtained either from umbilical cord blood or bone marrow. These cells can then be cultured in a laboratory to produce specialised cells, which can be put back into a patient.

A number of adult stem cell therapies already exist, particularly bone marrow transplants that are used to treat leukemia. In the future, scientists believe they could use stem cell treatments to treat many conditions including certain cancers, Parkinson's disease, spinal cord injuries, multiple sclerosis and muscle damage.

How Science Works

Should scientists be allowed to carry out stem cell research? It is expensive and some people believe it could be used for the wrong reasons.

Progress Check

1 What is the name for a group of similar cells?
2 An organ is made up of different tissues. True or false?
3 What is the job of the chloroplasts in a plant cell?
4 Why do human cells not contain chloroplasts?

4. Humans do not make their own food using energy from the Sun.
3. To absorb energy from the Sun.
1. Tissue 2. True

2.2 Human reproduction

Learning Summary

After studying this section you should be able to:

- describe the changes that take place during adolescence
- explain what happens during the menstrual cycle
- explain fertilisation and describe how a fertilised egg develops into a baby

Adolescence

New humans are created by **sexual reproduction**.

Key Point

In sexual reproduction a male sex cell joins with a female sex cell to create a new living thing.

Some plants and animals can reproduce without sex. This is called asexual reproduction. An example is growing a new plant by taking a cutting from an existing plant.

Before they can reproduce, children need to change into adults. This happens during **adolescence**.

In boys the main changes that take place between the ages of 11 and 14 are:
- They start to produce male sex cells (sperm).
- The voice becomes deeper.
- Hair grows around the **penis** and on the **scrotum**.
- The penis becomes larger.

In girls, adolescence may start earlier, from the age of 10. The main changes that take place are:
- They start to release female sex cells (ova) from the **ovaries**.
- **Breasts** develop.
- Hair grows around the **vulva**, the fleshy external opening to the **vagina**.
- A regular **menstrual cycle** begins, with **periods** each month.

The hair that grows around the penis and the vulva is thicker than the hair that grows on the head. It is called pubic hair.

Both boys and girls change emotionally during adolescence. They become sexually attracted to other people and are often concerned about whether they are sexually attractive to others.

Progress Check

1. Complete the sentences:
   In adolescence boys produce male sex cells called _____ .
   In adolescence girls release female sex cells called _____ .
2. Which of the following options is correct?
   In women, periods occur once each:
   A – day   **B** – week   **C** – month   **D** – year
3. What change takes place to a boy's penis during adolescence?

1. Sperm; eggs or ova   2. C   3. It becomes larger.

Menstruation

A period is a result of the **uterus** (womb) preparing itself each month to receive a fertilised egg.

The diagram shows the main parts of the female reproductive system.

Figure 2.03 The female reproductive system

In diagrams of the female reproductive system, pupils often confuse the cervix with the vulva. The vulva is the external entry to the vagina, and the cervix is the tube that leads to the uterus.

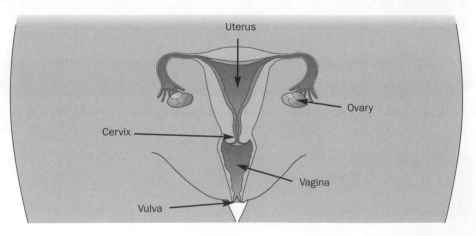

> Girls are born with thousands of unripened eggs, but adult males are continually making new sperm.

In the menstrual cycle:

- An egg ripens and is released from an ovary each month.
- As the egg travels slowly along the fallopian tube, the lining of the uterus thickens.
- If the egg enters the uterus unfertilised the thickened lining falls away.
- The unfertilised egg and the lining of the uterus pass out through the vagina – this is the period.

> The lining of the uterus is at its thickest as the egg enters the uterus from a fallopian tube.

The diagram shows the changes that take place during the menstrual cycle.

Figure 2.04 The menstrual cycle

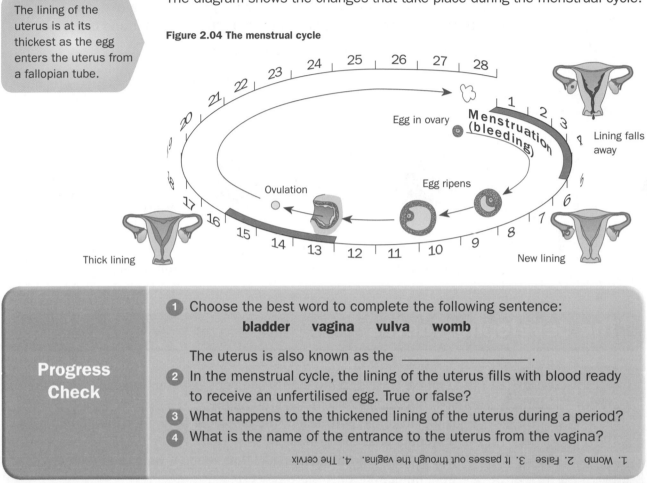

Progress Check

1. Choose the best word to complete the following sentence:

   bladder   vagina   vulva   womb

   The uterus is also known as the _____ .
2. In the menstrual cycle, the lining of the uterus fills with blood ready to receive an unfertilised egg. True or false?
3. What happens to the thickened lining of the uterus during a period?
4. What is the name of the entrance to the uterus from the vagina?

1. Womb   2. False   3. It passes out through the vagina.   4. The cervix

Fertilisation

The diagram shows the main parts of the male reproductive system.

> When the penis is erect, it is at the correct angle to fit into the vagina.

Figure 2.05 The male reproductive system

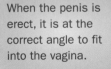

Sperm tube
Erectile tissue
Penis
Testis
Scrotum

During **sexual intercourse**:

- the **erectile tissue** becomes filled with blood, causing the penis to swell and become erect
- the penis is inserted into the vagina
- sperm from the **testes** flows through the sperm tube and out through the end of the penis
- the sperm are normally released at the **cervix**, the entrance to the uterus.

The sperm swim through the uterus and along the fallopian tubes. If they meet an egg in the fallopian tubes, fertilisation may take place.

Key Point	**Fertilisation** is the joining together, or fusion, of a male sex cell (sperm) and a female sex cell (ovum or egg).

When an egg is fertilised, one sperm enters the egg and the nuclei of the two cells join together. This single cell is the beginning of a new human. Its nucleus contains information from both the mother and the father.

The diagram shows what happens in fertilisation.

Figure 2.06 Fertilisation

Sperm

Nucleus

Tail breaks off

Head of sperm and nucleus fuse

The single cell divides and these cells divide several times as they travel along the fallopian tube to the uterus. Now it is an **embryo**.

The developing foetus

> The embryo becomes a foetus when it has recognisable human features.

> It is important to remember that the blood of the foetus and that of the mother never mix.

The embryo travels to the uterus and beds itself in the lining. Here the embryo develops into a foetus. The foetus:
- is joined to the **placenta** by the **umbilical cord**; food, oxygen and waste materials pass along the cord
- is surrounded by a watery liquid that keeps it warm and protects it from bumps

After nine months of **pregnancy**, the baby is born through the vagina.

A human baby is helpless at birth and relies on care from parents if it is to survive. Some animals produce babies that do not need a great deal of care from parents.

Figure 2.07 The developing foetus

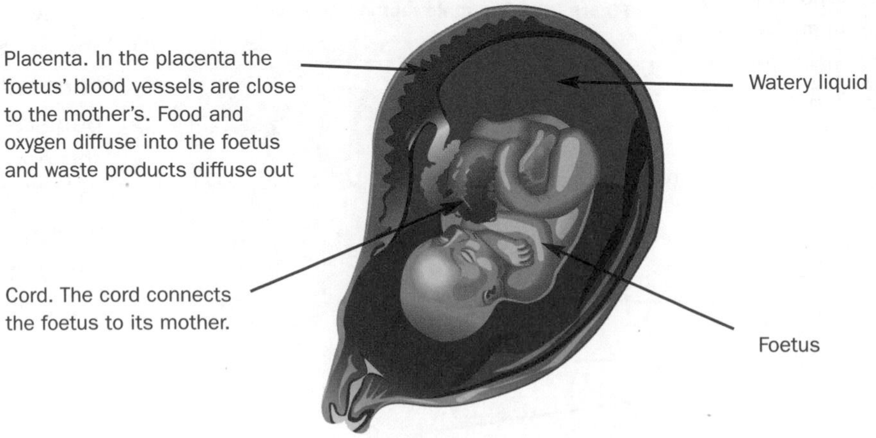

Placenta. In the placenta the foetus' blood vessels are close to the mother's. Food and oxygen diffuse into the foetus and waste products diffuse out

Cord. The cord connects the foetus to its mother.

Watery liquid

Foetus

2.3 Diet, drugs and disease

Learning Summary

After studying this section you should be able to:

- explain what is meant by a balanced diet
- recall that lungs, diaphragm, rib cage and associated muscles of the rib cage are essential for breathing
- describe the effects of smoking on the lungs and other body systems
- describe how alcohol and drugs affect the human body
- recall the names of different types of micro-organisms
- recall that some micro-organisms are useful and some are harmful
- describe how the body fights infectious diseases

Food and diet

People often take the word diet to mean food necessary to lose weight. We all have a diet. Your diet is the food you eat.

A balanced diet provides:
- everything required for growth of the body
- everything required for repair of the body
- enough energy for the body's activities

The human diet must contain **proteins**, **carbohydrates**, **fats**, **vitamins**, **minerals**, **fibre** and **water**.

The table gives information about these different food chemicals.

Food chemical	Benefit to the body	Source
Proteins	Provide amino acids for building and repairing the body	Meat, fish, milk, cheese
Carbohydrates includes sugar and starch	Provide energy	Bread, potatoes, cake
Fats	Store energy, give insulation	Butter, oil and margarine
Vitamins, e.g. vitamin C	Required in small quantities for good health	Fruit, vegetables
Minerals, e.g. iron	Required in small amounts for good health	Fruit, green vegetables

In addition to the food chemicals in the table, your diet should contain water and dietary fibre (roughage).

- **Fibre** is not digested, but helps in the production of faeces and prevents constipation. There is also evidence that fibre in the diet helps to retain water in the gut cavity and reduces the risk of bowel cancer.
- **Water** acts as a solvent, transports substances and provides a medium where reactions can take place.

Vitamins

Each **vitamin** has a particular job controlling a vital process in the body. Only small amounts are required to ensure good health.

The table gives some of the common vitamins and the jobs they do.

Vitamin	Good source	Use
A	green vegetables, butter, egg yolk, fish oils	healthy skin and membranes, prevents night blindness
B complex	yeast extract, liver, wholemeal bread	various, particularly respiration
C	citrus fruits, blackcurrants, vegetables	healthy skin, resistance to colds
D	butter, egg yolk, made in the skin (needs sunlight)	helps make bones

We now know how important it is to eat fruit and vegetables that provide a source of Vitamin C. Scurvy affected sailors on long voyages. The disease caused bleeding gums, weakness of muscles and, ultimately, death. It was prevented by giving sailors fruit juice to drink. Dr James Lind found this out in 1747. British ships going on a long journey took limes to prevent scurvy. This led to British sailors being called 'Limeys'.

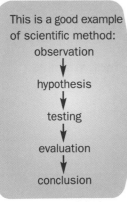

This is a good example of scientific method:

observation
↓
hypothesis
↓
testing
↓
evaluation
↓
conclusion

The first vitamin to be identified was vitamin B1. In 1896 a Dutch doctor, Dr Eilkman, was looking for a cure for a disease called beriberi. He noticed that some chickens in the hospital had a similar disease. He then noticed that the condition of the chickens changed when their food was changed from polished rice (rice with the outer husks removed) to whole grain rice (which contained the husks). He and his colleague, Dr Grijns, concluded that it must be a chemical in the husk that prevented beriberi.

In 1906 they boiled up some husks in water and used the solution to cure a pigeon that was suffering from beriberi. In 1934 scientists were able to identify the chemical in the husks and called it vitamin B1. In 1937 scientists were able to make vitamin B1 in the laboratory without having to extract it from rice husks.

Mineral salts

The table gives some examples of mineral salts needed in the human body. Like vitamins, they are needed only in small amounts.

Element	Good source	Use in the body
Ca (calcium)	cheese, milk	bones and teeth
F (fluorine)	toothpaste	hardening tooth enamel
Fe (iron	liver, green vegetables	part of haemoglobin in red blood cells
I (iodine)	table salt additive, sea food	thyroid gland
K (potassium)	green vegetables	nerve and muscle function
Na (sodium)	table salt	nerve and muscle function

Progress Check

1 What are the seven types of food chemical needed in a healthy diet?

2 A man is advised by his doctor to reduce the fat and to increase the fibre in his diet. Which form of potatoes in the list would be most suitable for him? Explain your choice.

Chipped potatoes, potato crisps, jacket potatoes, mashed potatoes, boiled potatoes.

3 Which foods are good sources of calcium?

1. Proteins, carbohydrates, fats, vitamins, minerals, fibre, water
2. Jacket potatoes – skins rich in fibre.   Chipped potatoes and potato crisps are cooked in fat and fat is absorbed. Mashed potato has fat added. Boiled potatoes has much less fibre.
3. Milk and cheese.

Breathing

Figure 2.08 Human respiratory pathway

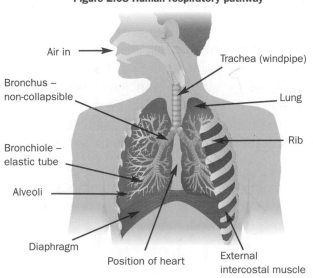

Air in

Bronchus – non-collapsible

Bronchiole – elastic tube

Alveoli

Diaphragm

Position of heart

Trachea (windpipe)

Lung

Rib

External intercostal muscle

Figure 2.08 shows the system that takes air into the lungs and expels waste air. It is called the **respiratory system**. The diagram shows the structure of the chest cavity (called the **thorax**).

The lungs are important in providing the oxygen to the bloodstream and removing the carbon dioxide.

The process of breathing is a mechanical process filling the lungs with air and then expelling waste air.

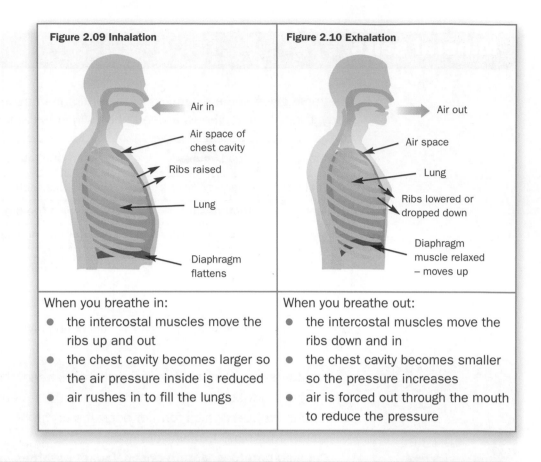

Figure 2.09 Inhalation	Figure 2.10 Exhalation
Air in Air space of chest cavity Ribs raised Lung Diaphragm flattens	Air out Air space Lung Ribs lowered or dropped down Diaphragm muscle relaxed – moves up
When you breathe in: ● the intercostal muscles move the ribs up and out ● the chest cavity becomes larger so the air pressure inside is reduced ● air rushes in to fill the lungs	When you breathe out: ● the intercostal muscles move the ribs down and in ● the chest cavity becomes smaller so the pressure increases ● air is forced out through the mouth to reduce the pressure

Effects of smoking

Tobacco contains a drug called nicotine. This drug speeds up the heart rate and raises blood pressure. Because of these changes a smoker has an increased risk of heart disease.

Other problems are caused when tobacco is smoked. The lungs have a mechanism to keep themselves clean. This involves producing a layer of mucus that is moved up and down the throat by moving hairs called cilia. Smoking slows down the movement of the cilia and produces more mucus. This mucus collects in the bronchioles (tiny tubes in the lungs) causing a 'smoker's cough'.

There are 50 million smokers in the United States of America. It is estimated that half of them will eventually die of smoking-related diseases.

Micro-organisms can get into the lungs more easily making diseases such as bronchitis more common. If micro-organisms are not cleared up, permanent damage to the lungs can occur. The bronchioles become narrower and this makes breathing more difficult. The person has to breathe faster to receive the same amount of oxygen. This illness, called **emphysema**, will eventually be fatal. Smoking also increases the chances of lung cancer.

Even being a non-smoker does not remove all of the risks of tobacco. It has been shown that breathing in smoke from a nearby smoker, known as '**passive smoking**', can lead to certain health risks.

Effects of alcohol

When alcohol is swallowed it quickly gets into the bloodstream. In small amounts it can boost confidence and change personality. Alcohol is also a depressant drug that slows down the drinker's reactions. Co-ordination is clumsier and the vision can be impaired.

For these reasons there is a severe limit on the concentration of alcohol permitted in a car driver's blood. Unfortunately, no driver can know how much alcohol they can drink and still remain 'below the limit' as each human body uses up alcohol at different rates.

The following drinks contain one unit of alcohol.

Figure 2.11 Drinks containing one unit of alcohol.

Half a pint of beer   Glass of wine   Single whisky

Effects of drugs

Like tobacco and alcohol, other drugs can affect the nervous system, which controls the operation of the body. There are four types of drug:

1 **Sedatives**, which slow the brain down and make the person sleepy.

2 **Stimulants**, which speed up the brain and make the person more alert.

3 **Hallucinogens**, which cause a person to have experiences that are different from real life.

4 **Painkillers**, which remove our sense of pain.

Drugs can seriously affect health and can be addictive.

Microbes and disease

There are other kinds of micro-organism. One is fungi. These too can be...
- harmful, e.g. producing athlete's foot
- helpful, e.g. as a source of antibiotics

Ill health can be caused by a variety of micro-organisms, including bacteria and viruses entering the body. Bacteria can enter the body through ears, eyes, mouth, nose, anus, penis/vagina or a cut in the skin. Once in the body they can multiply.

The table summarises some of the similarities and some of the differences between bacteria and viruses.

	Bacterium	Virus
	Cell wall and cell membrane	Protein coat
	Has genes but no nucleus	Has genes
	Has cytoplasm	No cytoplasm
	Can reproduce outside living cells	Can only reproduce inside living cells
	Destroyed by antibiotics	Not destroyed by antibiotics
	Bacteria produce toxins (poisons)	Viruses damage the cells in which they reproduce

How the body prevents micro-organisms entering

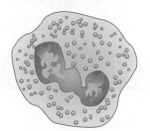

Figure 2.12 White blood cell

Students frequently write that white blood cells eat the microbes. This is not strictly correct – 'engulf' is the best word to use.

The body prevents micro-organisms from entering in several ways:
- The skin acts as a barrier.
- The breathing organs produce sticky mucus to trap microbes.
- Blood platelets produce clots to seal cuts.

White blood cells have a defensive role:

1. They engulf and destroy microbes.

2. They produce antibodies that destroy microbes.

3. They produce antitoxins that counteract the toxins produced by microbes.

Figure 2.13 White blood cell engulfing bacteria

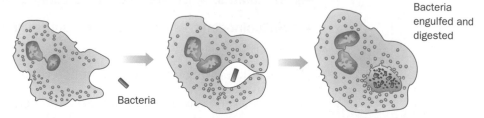

Bacteria

Bacteria engulfed and digested

Once we have had a particular disease, the body knows how to produce antibodies and so the white blood cells can produce them quickly before the disease takes hold. We are said to be **immune** to that microbe.

Louis Pasteur (1822–1895)

In 1765, Lazzaro Spallanzani showed that food would not go bad if the microbes in it were destroyed. One way of killing the microbes in soup was to boil it.

Louis Pasteur was a French scientist who studied microbes and proved that they were responsible for the process of decay.

Pasteur was able to isolate the bacteria that caused diseases such as cattle anthrax and chicken cholera.

Key Point

Bacteria are not all bad. They play an important role in many processes, for example sewage treatment.

Antibiotics were first discovered by accident. Sir Alexander Fleming noticed in 1928 that staphylococcus (a bacterium) in contact with a mould disappeared. He rightly concluded that there was an antibacterial substance in the mould. This was later found to be penicillin. Fleming did not succeed in making penicillin, that was done 15 years later by HW Florrey and EB Chain. The ease with which penicillin can be destroyed is one reason why it was difficult to make. Since then the use of penicillin and other antibiotics has saved millions of lives.

How Science Works

Many important materials were discovered by accident, e.g. polythene. Scientists repeat and try to reproduce the results.

Sexually transmitted infections (STIs)

Sexually transmitted infections (STIs), sometimes called sexually transmitted diseases (STDs), are transferred from one person to another by sexual contact. There are over 20 diseases that can be transferred in this way. Some are transferred by bacteria and some by viruses.

STIs include Chlamydia, Gonorrhea and HIV/Aids.

There are 400 000 new cases of STIs reported each year, with a large proportion of these in young people.

Contracting STIs can result in infertility and serious illness including death. At the first symptoms medical attention should be obtained.

The chances of sexually transmitted infections being contracted can be reduced by…
● abstinence from sexual activity
● avoiding sexual contact with different partners
● always using condoms.

Progress Check

1. Milk is pasteurised before being sold. What is this process and why is it done?
2. A doctor will not prescribe antibiotics to cure a virus. Why not?
3. Why is it important to take all of the antibiotics prescribed for a bacterial infection?
4. The body uses up one unit of alcohol each hour. A person is drinking heavily until 2 am. Why is it unwise for the person to drive to work the next morning?

4. The person may still be 'over the limit' in the morning.
3. Antibiotics kill bacteria. If the full course is not taken the few bacteria remaining can then multiply.
2. Antibiotics have no effect on a virus.
1. Milk is heated to a high temperature for a short period and then cooled. This kills bacteria.

2.4 Classification

Learning Summary	**After studying this section you should be able to:**
	● recall how animals and plants can be classified

Classification of animals

All living things can be divided into kingdoms. Two of these are the animal kingdom and the plant kingdom. Kingdoms are then divided into phyla (singular phylum).

There are millions of different species of plants and animals and new species are being discovered all the time. Rather than try to study each one separately, it is sensible to put them together and study them as groups.

For example, if we consider the animal kingdom, we can divide all animals into two major groups:
● animals with backbones (called **vertebrates**)
● animals without backbones (called **invertebrates**)

Progress Check

① Which animals are vertebrates and which are invertebrates?

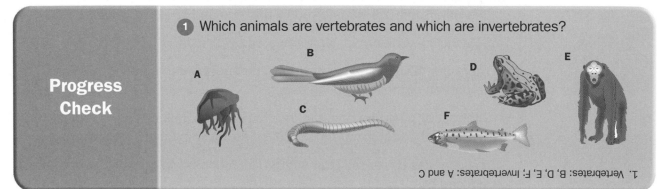

1. Vertebrates: B, D, E, F; Invertebrates: A and C

We can divide vertebrates further, according to whether the animal has a body temperature the same as its surroundings (called cold-blooded) or whether the animal is able to keep its body temperature the same on hot or cold days (called warm-blooded).

Cold-blooded animals cannot use internal processes to control their body temperature. However, cold-blooded animals, e.g. a snake, can warm up their bodies by basking in the sun.

The table lists common groups of vertebrates divided into cold-blooded and warm-blooded classes.

Cold-blooded	Warm-blooded
Fish	Birds
Amphibians	Mammals
Reptiles	

Each of these classes has its own characteristics.

Fish   Paired fins; gills.
Amphibians   Slimy skin; spend some of their lives in water.
Reptiles   Dry scaly skin; lay eggs on land.
Birds   Feathers; lay eggs on land.
Mammals   Hair; provide milk for young from special glands.

We can classify invertebrates in a similar way, producing a number of different groups of phyla.

Phylum	Feature
Protozoa	made of one cell, e.g. amoeba
Sponges	animals made of similar cells loosely joined together
Cnidaria	body walls made of two layers of cells, e.g. jellyfish, sea anemones
Flat worms	flattened worm-like shape, e.g. tape worm
Annelida	worms made of segments, e.g. earthworms
Arthropoda	jointed legs, bodies made of segments; includes spiders, insects, centipedes
Mollusca	no segments; a fleshy pad on which they crawl, e.g. slug, snail
Echinodermata	star-shaped pattern, spiny skin, e.g. starfish

Figure 2.14 summarises the family tree of animals. The number in each case is an approximation of the number of different species.

Figure 2.14 Classification of animals

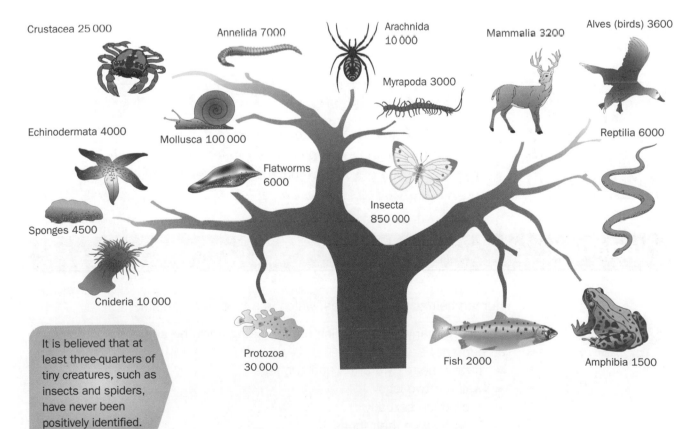

Crustacea 25 000
Annelida 7000
Arachnida 10 000
Mammalia 3200
Alves (birds) 3600
Myrapoda 3000
Echinodermata 4000
Mollusca 100 000
Reptilia 6000
Flatworms 6000
Sponges 4500
Insecta 850 000
Cnideria 10 000
Protozoa 30 000
Fish 2000
Amphibia 1500

It is believed that at least three-quarters of tiny creatures, such as insects and spiders, have never been positively identified.

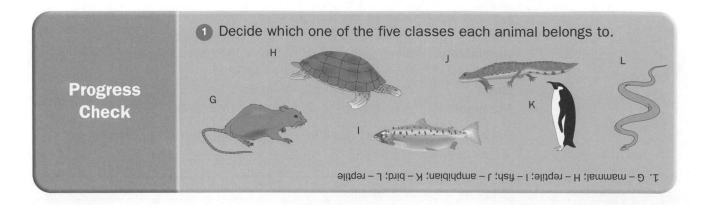

Progress Check

1 Decide which one of the five classes each animal belongs to.

1. G – mammal; H – reptile; I – fish; J – amphibian; K – bird; L – reptile

Classification of plants

Plants can be classified in a similar way as animals.

One way of dividing plants into classes is shown below.

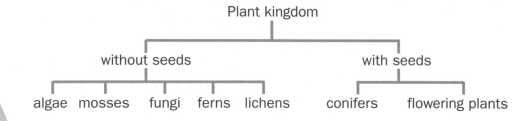

> Mosses do not have a waterproof layer. This confines them to damp environments.

Green plants can be subdivided into those with vascular tissues (xylem and phloem) and complex leaves with a waterproof cuticle and those without.

2.5 Variation

Learning Summary

After studying this section you should be able to:

- describe how individuals of one species (e.g. humans) vary
- describe how animals and plants vary to form different species
- describe the use of selective breeding and genetic engineering

Variation

Human beings are a species, which is a type of organism.

There are many ways in which human beings are the same. For example, all humans:

- have a head, two arms and two legs
- walk on two legs
- reproduce sexually
- breathe with their lungs

The list is endless although there are some individual exceptions.

Now think about the ways in which human beings differ. Some obvious examples are...

- height
- weight
- colour of hair or skin or eyes.

Again, the list is endless.

Figure 2.15 Human beings can differ

Key Point	Differences between species and between individuals of a species is called **variation**.

Nature or nurture

What determines whether you are a human being, rather than a fly or a cat or a rabbit? The answer is the **genetic information** from your parents. This information was contained in the sperm and the egg that joined at the instant you were created. The same information is contained in all the nuclei of your body cells. This information determines:

- the colour of your hair
- your sex (i.e. whether you are male or female)
- the colour of your eyes

It also influences a number of other things, such as:

- how tall you are
- your body shape
- your weight

> If you have some family photographs, you can compare your own physical appearance with that of your parents when they were the same age.

However, genetics is not the only factor that determines your height, shape and weight. These are also influenced by **environmental factors** such as:

- your diet – whether you eat a balanced diet or a lot of fatty foods and chocolate
- exercise – for example, whether you walk or cycle to school or travel in a car
- physical activity – whether you take an active part in sport or prefer to watch television

There are some aspects of your physical appearance that have nothing to do with genetics – they are totally controlled by environmental factors. These include:

- the length of your hair
- whether you wear an earring
- the length of your finger nails

Most of the differences between human beings are due to a combination of genetic and environmental factors – **nature** and **nurture**.

This number is larger than the number of people who have ever lived.

You will not have an exact double during your lifetime.

Have you noticed that brothers and sisters in the same family are not identical? Unless they are identical twins, the chances of parents having two identical children is about one in 1 800 000 000 000 000. This number is very large.

Variation is caused by different mixes of genes and by mutation.

There are two types of variation:

1 Discontinuous variation

This enables us to separate the population into different, clearly distinguished groups, e.g. by blood group. We can sort the blood groups of individuals into four main groups – A, B, AB and O. No one falls between two groups (e.g. a mixture of groups A and O).

Another example of discontinuous variation is albinism. This is a complete lack of skin pigment caused by the difference of a single gene.

2 Continuous variation

Sometimes we cannot see clearly different groups.

For example, if we were to measure the length of the middle finger of the right hand of 30 children, the results could not be clearly put into groups. Height and weight are other good examples.

Figure 2.16 shows the kind of variation that could be seen in the heights of a sample of men.

Figure 2.16 Variation in the heights of a sample of men

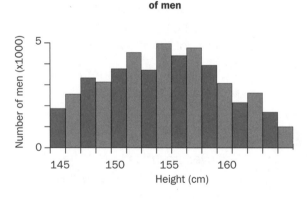

Whether the variation in height of these men is due to the genes they inherited from parents or the way the men have lived (environment) is a question that has interested scientists for many years.

In order to investigate this, scientists have studied identical twins. Identical twins have exactly the same genes because they are both formed from a single fertilised egg. This egg splits into two after it has been fertilised and two identical embryos are formed. So, any differences in identical twins cannot be due to differences in their genes. Any differences must be due to the influence of the environment, such as amount and quality of food.

Studying identical twins that are separated shortly after birth and reared separately can give interesting information. If the twins still have similar characteristics, it suggests that inheritance was the main influence. If characteristics are very different, it suggests that environment was the main influence.

Mutations

The copying of chromosomes when cells divide is very complicated and mistakes can occur. These mistakes are called **mutations**. Mutations can be caused by radiation and by some chemicals.

Down's syndrome is caused by a mutation. Children with Down's syndrome have an extra chromosome. This occurs most frequently when the mother is older and the cell division to produce eggs has not occurred properly.

> Most mutations are harmful but good mutations are possible.

Progress Check

1. Which is correct, **A**, **B** or **C**?
   A species is:
   A – an animal   **B** – a plant   **C** – a type of organism
2. Variation describes the ways in which different organisms are similar. True or false?
3. Which **two** options are correct?
   A Genetic information is inherited by an organism from its parents.
   B Genetic information is controlled by the environment.
   C Genetic information is contained in every nucleus in body cells.
4. Is the colour of a person's skin controlled by genetic factors, environmental factors or both?
5. Give **two** environmental factors that can affect your weight.
6. A study was carried out on a hundred pairs of identical twins. 50 pairs of twins were brought up together, and the other 50 pairs were separated at birth and brought up apart. Heights and weights were recorded at the same age. The results are shown in the table.

Difference in characteristic	Twins brought up together	Twins brought up apart
Average height in m	1.3	1.4
Average weight in kg	20	30

   (a) Look at the heights. Is there much difference between twins brought up together and separated? What does this suggest?
   (b) Is there much difference in weights? What does this suggest?

1. C 2. False 3. A and C 4. Both 5. Diet and the amount of exercise that you take. 6. (a) No, little difference. Suggests variation largely due to genetics. (b) Yes, big difference. Suggests variation due to differences in the environment.

Selective breeding

Selective breeding is a method of improving the quality of plants and animals. It involves selecting good examples to cross and then choosing the best specimens. Repeating this process many times produces better plants or animals.

Figure 2.17 shows how a farmer might produce sheep with thicker wool by selective breeding.

Figure 2.17 Selective breeding to produce sheep with thicker wool

The farmer picks (selects) parents with thick fleeces.

The farmer breeds these parents to produce offspring.

Some of the offspring will have thicker fleeces than others.

More of these offspring than in step 3. This continues until all the sheep have thick fleeces.

The farmer selects the sheep with thicker fleeces and breeds them.

Genetic engineering

Genetic engineering is a technique used by scientists to alter an organism by inserting **genes** from another organism.

Examples

① In some countries people suffer from a lack of vitamin A in their diet. This lack of vitamin A leads to 500 000 children going blind every year. A genetically modified form of rice has been developed that contains vitamin A. This Golden Rice, so called because of its colour, could be used to overcome this problem of vitamin A deficiency in some countries.

② Genetic engineering can be used to make insulin (a protein used by diabetics) in large quantities. The gene for human insulin production is inserted into the chromosomes of bacteria. The bacteria are grown inside large containers called bioreactors. The bacteria produce insulin, which is then extracted and purified.

How Science Works

Should scientists carry out genetic engineering? Some people believe this is tampering with nature and may produce harmful products. On the other hand, genetic engineering may help feed the world's increasing population and cure illnesses.

Progress Check

① Fruit trees have been grown by selective breeding that are only 2 metres high (compared with normal trees that are 5–6 metres high). What are the advantages to the farmer of these shorter trees?

② What are the advantages of growing wheat that has shorter, sturdier stems with more seeds on each stem?

1. Easier to pick fruit; Less damage caused by wind; Easier to spray and prune; More trees can be grown in a given area
2. Less easily blown over; Plants not wasting energy growing long stems; Higher yield.

2.6 Behaviour

Learning Summary

After studying this section you should be able to:

- describe what is meant by behaviour and be able to name types of behaviour
- describe different types of behaviour
- outline methods that can be used to study behaviour

Types of behaviour

Behaviour is the action or reaction of an organism, usually in relation to its environment.

The study of animal behaviour is called **ethology**. The study of human behaviour is called **psychology**.

There are different types of behaviour.

Instinct

If you touch a spider's web well away from where the spider is, the spider will move towards the disturbance. This is an **instinct**. The spider may believe that the disturbance of the web is linked with a fly hitting the web and providing food. Other instincts may protect the organism from danger, choose a mate, etc.

A **reflex** is a type of instinct. It happens automatically when a particular stimulus is made.

For example, if your hand accidentally touches a hot saucepan, you automatically remove your hand by a reflex action. This type of action does not need to be learned.

On the other hand when your telephone rings, you answer it. This is not a reflex action. It is something you have learned to do. It is **learned behaviour**.

Instinct is the inherited and unlearned response to a stimulus. With animals it is often not possible to overcome these instincts. With humans it is possible to overcome these instincts and follow certain behaviour.

Imprinting

Many animals are able to walk soon after they are born.

For example, goslings (young geese) are able to walk soon after they are hatched. Within a few days they are able to swim. They recognise their mother because of **imprinting** and they follow their mother for food and protection. Ducklings will follow the first moving object they meet after hatching. They become socially attached to this object and treat it as their mother.

Konrad Lorenz (1903–1989) was an Austrian scientist who studied animal behaviour. He discovered that if he hatched geese eggs in an incubator, the goslings became imprinted on him. They followed him around and they preferred his company to that of other geese.

Conditioning

Conditioning is when the response to a stimulus is different from the natural one. It is a type of **learned behaviour**.

Ivan Pavlov (1849–1936) was a Russian scientist who investigated conditioning in dog studies. When dogs are given food they produce extra saliva (which is needed to help digest the food). Pavlov rang a bell each time food was brought into the room and a dog was fed. The dog began to associate the sound of the bell with food and eventually the dog produced extra saliva when the bell was rung, even if no food was brought in.

This is not a natural response. The behaviour has been learned. It is called a **conditioned response**.

Imitating

Imitation is a type of behaviour where one animal copies another animal. Imitation helps an animal to learn how to do new things. For example, some scientists have observed that some chimpanzees can imitate each other.

Humans show many of the same types of behaviour as other animals. But human behaviour is often more complex because we are more intelligent and aware of ourselves.

Investigating behaviour

It is possible to investigate behaviour in field studies or in the laboratory. Providing that observations and measurements are possible, an experiment can be devised. Experiments that take place outside the laboratory are field studies.

For example, an experiment could be devised to compare the number of insects in full sun and in shade. Areas in full sun and in shade could be chosen and the number of insects in each area counted. This investigation is considering what difference light makes to insect density. However, in experiments like this it is difficult to exclude other differences. For example, there would be a temperature difference, which could also affect the number of insects.

It is possible to tag birds and animals in the wild and track their movements.

Experiments may be devised in the laboratory to analyse animal behaviour.

Progress Check

1. Which type of human behaviour is shown by the following behaviour?
   (a) Young people who start smoking when their friends start.
   (b) Advertising a product by linking it to a famous sportsman.

1. (a) Imitating (b) Conditioning

2.7 Environment and feeding relationships

Learning Summary	After studying this section you should be able to:
	<ul><li>describe how a habitat provides the environment that animals and plants need to survive</li><li>explain how the animals and plants in a habitat depend on each other</li><li>describe how some organisms are adapted to survive changes in their habitats</li></ul>

Habitats

A pile of rotting wood provides all these things for a colony of woodlice.

For much of the year, we live indoors. Most plants and animals live outdoors. The region where a particular plant or animal lives is called its **habitat**. A habitat provides:

- food
- shelter
- a place to reproduce

Key Point

A **habitat** is a place where an organism lives, feeds and reproduces.

In a large garden there can be a number of habitats. For example, a hedge:

- Provides food for worms and other soil-based animals that feed on the dead leaves.
- Provides shelter for birds and hedgehogs.
- The birds and hedgehogs eat the animals that feed off the hedge.

Other habitats could include a tree or a pond, or an area of bushes or flowers.

Progress Check

1. What are the three important things that a habitat provides?
2. Plants are important to a pond habitat because they add oxygen to the water. True or false?
3. How does the fox's habitat provide it with food?

3. The fox's prey, smaller animals, live in the habitat.
1. Food, shelter and a place to reproduce. 2. True

How plants and animals are adapted

You will often come across questions in tests about how different plants and animals are adapted to their habitat.

The animals in any habitat have special features that enable them to live there. For example, a fish can live in a pond but a fox could not.

To live in a pond a fish needs:
- fins so that it can move through the water
- a tail so that it can control its direction of movement
- gills for gas exchange

A fox needs:
- strong hind legs so that it can run fast to overtake its prey
- canine teeth to tear flesh when it feeds
- lungs for gas exchange

Bluebells and anemones are woodland plants that flower in spring.

Plants are also adapted with special features that suit their habitat. Woodland plants often develop and flower in the spring when light can penetrate through the trees. In summer, when there is little light coming through the trees, they are dormant.

The plants in a pond grow most vigorously in summer when there is the greatest amount of sunlight, which gives them energy for making food and growth. They are adapted to absorb energy from the Sun by floating on the water or having long stems so that their leaves are close to the surface of the water.

Feeding

Plants obtain essential vitamins and minerals from the soil.

Food is important to all plants and animals. It provides the energy needed to keep their organs working and to allow movement and growth. It also provides animals with the essential vitamins and minerals needed by different organs in the body.

Key Point

The key difference between plants and animals is that plants make their own food.

Plants use **carbon dioxide** from the air and **water** from the soil to manufacture food in the form of **glucose**, a simple sugar.
- Plants are called **producers** because they make all the food for the animals in a food chain.
- Animals such as worms and slugs that feed directly off plant material are called **primary consumers**.
- **Secondary consumers** feed off primary consumers.
- **Tertiary consumers** feed off secondary consumers.

Some animals, called **herbivores**, feed off plants. Other animals, called **carnivores**, feed off other animals. There are also animals, such as humans, that feed off both plants and other animals. These are called **omnivores**.

The feeding relationships in a habitat are shown by a **food web**, which consists of a number of **food chains**.

The diagram shows a food web based on an oak tree as the **producer**.

Figure 2.18 A food web

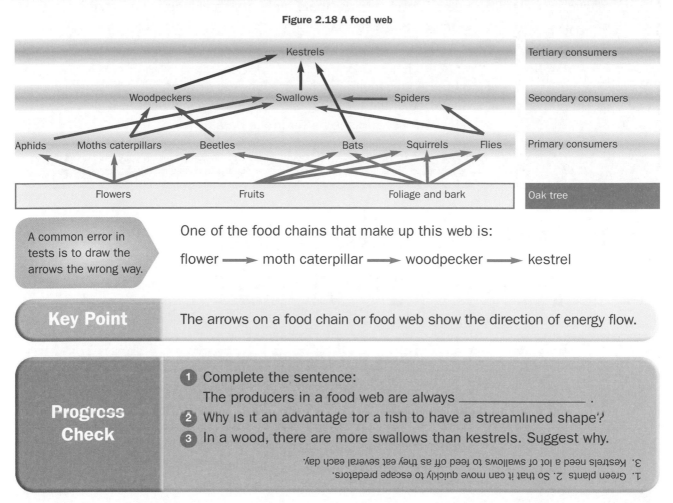

A common error in tests is to draw the arrows the wrong way.

One of the food chains that make up this web is:

flower ⟶ moth caterpillar ⟶ woodpecker ⟶ kestrel

Key Point

The arrows on a food chain or food web show the direction of energy flow.

Progress Check

1. Complete the sentence:
   The producers in a food web are always _____ .
2. Why is it an advantage for a fish to have a streamlined shape?
3. In a wood, there are more swallows than kestrels. Suggest why.

3. Kestrels need a lot of swallows to feed off as they eat several each day.
1. Green plants 2. So that it can move quickly to escape predators.

Changes in the environment

If you observe a habitat such as a hedge or a tree in a garden, you will notice that changes are continually taking place.

Each day there are changes in the:
- light intensity
- temperature
- moisture level

Over the course of a year there are even greater variations in all these factors. These changes can affect the:
- number of organisms in a habitat
- type of organisms in a habitat
- activity of the organisms in a habitat

Evergreen trees often have needle-shaped leaves to minimise water loss.

To survive in a changing habitat, organisms need to be adapted to cope with the extreme conditions. Many trees lose leaves in winter to reduce the loss of heat and water – a tree may not be able to take in water if the ground is frozen. Insects burrow into the ground or leaf litter, and their offspring survive the winter as eggs. Large animals, such as squirrels, build up a store of food to help them to survive.

1 In a cool wet summer there are more snails than in a hot, dry summer. Suggest why.

2 How does burrowing into the ground help an insect to survive the winter?

3 All trees lose their leaves in winter. True or false?

4 Say whether the following is true or false: Owls hunt at night because they can see better in the dark.

1. Snails need cool, damp conditions to reproduce. In hot weather they die and do not reproduce.
2. The ground insulates the insect and stops it from freezing.
3. False 4. False

2.8 Respiration and photosynthesis

Learning Summary

After studying this section you should be able to:

- recall that glucose and oxygen are needed by human cells for respiration
- describe how glucose and oxygen are transported to cells
- explain the role of the lungs
- describe the differences between inhaled and exhaled air
- recall that respiration takes place in other living organisms
- recall that green plants produce glucose in the leaves by photosynthesis
- describe how leaf cells close to the upper surface are adapted for photosynthesis
- recall that some glucose produced during photosynthesis is stored as starch
- explain why green plants are important for the environment

Respiration in human cells

Respiration is the process that takes place in all cells to release energy from glucose and oxygen. The glucose and oxygen reach the cells in the blood supply.

In the process of respiration, carbon dioxide and water are produced. Carbon dioxide is transported away from the cells in the blood.

Key Point

The word equation for respiration is:

glucose + oxygen $\longrightarrow$ carbon dioxide + water + energy

Respiration is a process that can be compared to burning.

The table compares the processes of respiration in cells with burning a carbon compound as fuel.

Respiration in cells	Burning a carbon compound such as fuel
uses food containing carbon, e.g. glucose	uses fuel containing carbon
uses oxygen	uses oxygen
produces carbon dioxide and water as wastes	produces carbon dioxide and water as wastes
releases energy, some as heat, some locked up	releases energy, most as heat, some as light

What is the role of the lungs?

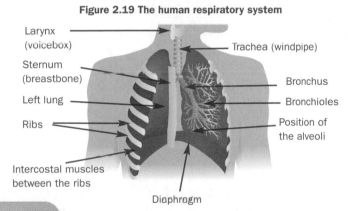

Figure 2.19 The human respiratory system

Larynx (voicebox)
Trachea (windpipe)
Sternum (breastbone)
Bronchus
Left lung
Bronchioles
Ribs
Position of the alveoli
Intercostal muscles between the ribs
Diaphragm

The diagram shows the human respiratory system. The lungs provide a means of getting oxygen into the bloodstream and removing the waste carbon dioxide.

Students frequently confuse respiration and breathing. Breathing is the mechanical process of inhaling and exhaling air. Respiration takes place in all the cells.

Air enters the lungs, which consist of branched tubes ending in millions of tiny sacs called **alveoli**. The walls of the alveoli are extremely thin and they have a very large surface area. Oxygen can diffuse through the alveoli into the blood and carbon dioxide can diffuse from the blood into the alveoli.

Students frequently forget that respiration takes place in plants because photosynthesis is so dominant in sunlight.

Figure 2.20 The blood supply to air sacs

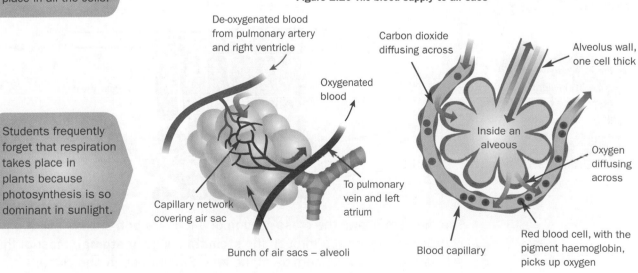

De-oxygenated blood from pulmonary artery and right ventricle
Carbon dioxide diffusing across
Alveolus wall, one cell thick
Oxygenated blood
Inside an alveous
Oxygen diffusing across
Capillary network covering air sac
To pulmonary vein and left atrium
Bunch of air sacs – alveoli
Blood capillary
Red blood cell, with the pigment haemoglobin, picks up oxygen

Photosynthesis

Figure 2.21 Parts of a plant

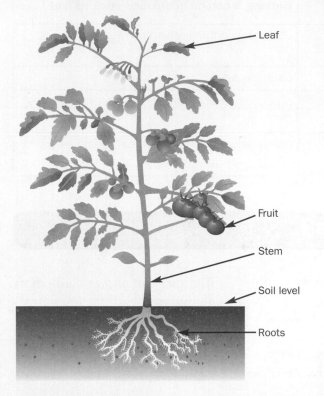

Leaf

Fruit

Stem

Soil level

Roots

The diagram shows the parts of a plant.

The roots anchor the plant in the soil. They also take water and important dissolved minerals from the soil. The water and dissolved minerals travel through hollow tubes in the stems to the leaves.

The leaves are the 'factories' of the plant. Here **photosynthesis** takes place, producing food for the plant.

Photosynthesis involves the reaction of water and carbon dioxide to produce glucose and oxygen. The oxygen is released into the atmosphere and the glucose is stored in the plant as starch. This process takes place in sunlight and in the presence of the green pigment, chlorophyll, which is a catalyst.

Key Point

The word equation for photosynthesis is:

$$\text{carbon dioxide} + \text{water} + \text{energy} \xrightarrow[\text{chlorophyll}]{\text{sunlight}} \text{glucose} + \text{oxygen}$$

The word equation for photosynthesis is the reverse of the word equation for respiration.

Leaves usually have a large area to absorb the maximum amount of light. They are thin so that carbon dioxide does not have to travel far through the leaf. The veins in a leaf give some support and provide the leaf with a supply of water.

Figure 2.22 Cross-section of a leaf

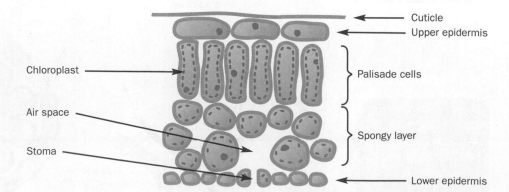

Cuticle

Upper epidermis

Chloroplast

Palisade cells

Air space

Spongy layer

Stoma

Lower epidermis

Photosynthesis takes place in daylight. Respiration takes place all the time but is not noticed during the day.

The diagram shows the cross-section of a leaf. Carbon dioxide needed for photosynthesis enters through the **stomata** (singular **stoma**). Most of the stomata are on the underside of the leaf. Stomata open and close.

Oxygen and water escape through the stomata. The stomata close at night to prevent too much loss of water.

The waxy layer on the surface of the leaf, called the **cuticle**, prevents evaporation of water from the surface. Below the cuticle there is a single layer of tightly-fitting cells called the **epidermis**. The **palisade cells**, below the epidermis but still near the surface of the leaf, contain a large number of **chloroplasts**. Chloroplasts contain the chlorophyll, and it is here that photosynthesis occurs.

The spongy layer contains large cells with irregular shapes. There are large gaps between the cells. Oxygen and carbon dioxide can be stored here.

Experiments showing photosynthesis often collect the oxygen produced.

The apparatus in the diagram shows a gas being produced. Larger volumes of gas could be collected in a gas syringe.

Photosynthesis is an important process as it replaces oxygen in the atmosphere.

Figure 2.23 Experiment to show photosynthesis

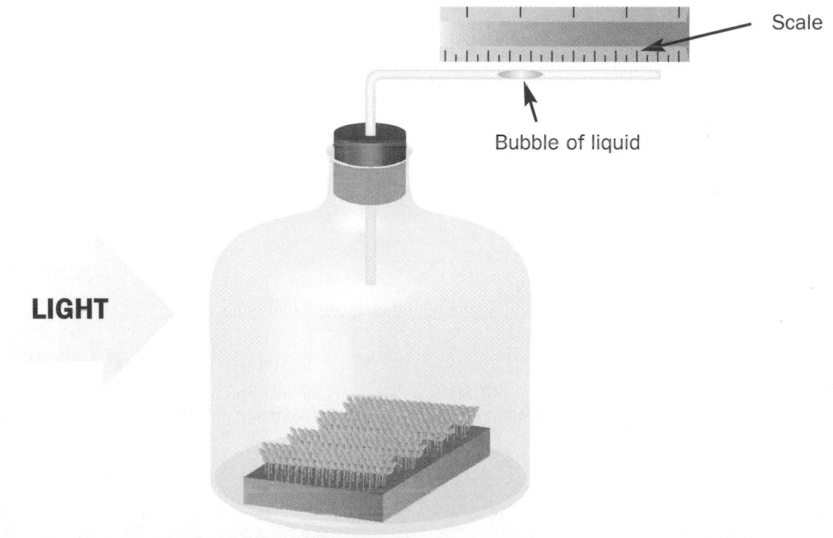

Scale

Bubble of liquid

LIGHT

Progress Check

① Finish the table by adding words from the list.

**Palisade cells   Spongy mesophyll cells   Stomata
Waxy cuticle**

Part of leaf	What it does
	Helps waterproof the leaf
	The holes through which gases get in and out
	Most photosynthesis occurs here
	Loosely packed cells that store gases

1. waxy cuticle, stomata, palisade cell, spongy mesophyll cells

Assessment questions

1. The diagram shows part of a food web in a pond.

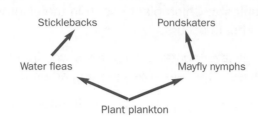

    (a) What is the producer in this food web?

    _____ [1]

    (b) How many of the organisms shown in the food web are animals?

    _____ [1]

    (c) How many of the organisms shown in the food web are fish?

    _____ [1]

    (d) A chemical is used to kill the plant plankton. Explain what happens to the numbers of
    the other organisms shown in the food web.

    _____

    _____ [2]

2. Choose words from this list to answer the questions that follow.

    cervix   fallopian tubes   ovary   testicle   uterus   vagina

    (a) Which word in the list is **not** part of the female reproductive system?

    testicle _____ [1]

    (b) Which part of the female reproductive system is the entrance from the vagina into
    the uterus?

    cervix _____ [1]

    (c) Which part of the female reproductive system produces eggs?

    ovary _____ [1]

    (d) Which part of the female reproductive system is where eggs and sperm meet?

    uterus _____ [1]

    (e) Which part of the female reproductive system prepares itself to receive the
    fertilised egg?

    fallopian tube _____ [1]

Assessment questions

Levels 5–6

3. **(a)** Mary wants to produce some new geraniums. She has some tall, spindly plants from the previous year. She looks in a catalogue and finds she can buy geranium seeds.

Write down two advantages and two disadvantages of making new plants from cuttings over growing new plants from seed.

_____

_____

_____ **[4]**

(b) Some of the geraniums have variegated leaves. These have patterns of yellow and green on them.

(i) Why does photosynthesis only take place on the green parts of the leaf and not the yellow?

_____

_____ **[2]**

(ii) Write down the word equation for photosynthesis.

_____ **[2]**

4. The diagram shows a cell.

(a) How can you tell that the cell is from a plant and not from an animal? Give two reasons.

An animal cell doesn't have a cell wall or
Chloroplast· **[2]**

(b) Which of the labelled parts of the cell:

(i) controls all the activity of the cell?

nucleus **[1]**

(ii) gives the cell a fixed shape?

vacuole **[1]**

(iii) absorbs the energy needed for the plant to make food?

_____ **[1]**

Assessment questions

(c) The diagram shows another cell from the plant.

Nucleus

Cell membrane

Cell wall

    (i) Which part of the plant is this cell taken from?

    _____ **[1]**

    (ii) What feature of the cell enables it to do its job?

    _____

    _____ **[1]**

Levels 7–8

5. Over the past 50 years the average yield of milk from a Fresian cow has increased by over 100%. Suggest and explain reasons why this has happened.

_____

_____

_____

_____

_____

_____ **[4]**

6. In daylight, green plants make food by photosynthesis.

    (a) Finish the symbol equation to summarise the process of photosynthesis.

        CO_2 + H_2O $\longrightarrow$

         [2]

    (b) Oxygen is the waste product of this process. How does the plant release this waste product?

    _____

    _____

    _____ **[2]**

Assessment questions

(c) The graph shows the amount of sugar produced by a tomato plant growing in a greenhouse over a period of days.

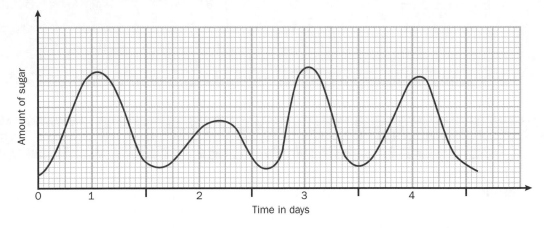

(i) Suggest which variable changes explain the varying amounts of sugar produced.

_____

_____ **[1]**

(ii) What could the grower do to increase the rate of sugar production? Assume the temperature is fixed and there is a constant supply of water.

_____

_____ **[1]**

3 Chemical and material behaviour

			Studied	Revised	Assessment questions
3.1	**The particle model**	– Classify materials as solids, liquids and gases – Using a particle model to explain observations			
3.2	**Atoms and elements**	– Elements – Classifying the elements			
3.3	**Compounds**	– Elements combining to form compounds			
3.4	**Metals and non-metals**	– Dividing elements into metals and non-metals			
3.5	**Acids and bases**	– What are acids and bases? – Detecting acids and bases – Neutralisation			

3.1 The particle model

Learning Summary

After studying this section you should be able to:

- classify materials as solids, liquids or gases
- explain that all substances are made of particles
- describe the movement and arrangement of particles in solids, liquids and gases
- use the particle model to explain some observations

Classify materials as solids, liquids and gases

Materials can be classified as solids, liquids or gases. However, all materials are made up from tiny particles.

The word **material** is often used to describe a type of fabric, such as cotton. In Science it is used to describe anything around you. Clay, water and air are all materials.

Many physical properties can be explained using a particle model. The idea of matter being made of particles was first proposed by the ancient Greek, Democritus, about 2500 years ago. His ideas were largely forgotten; they were purely a hypothesis with no evidence to support them. Only in 1803 did John Dalton propose his atomic theory. Dalton's model of particles explained many of the physical properties of substances he observed.

Particle model of solids, liquids and gases

The three pictures below give a very good idea of how very tiny particles are arranged and move in solids, liquids and gases. These particles are so small they cannot be seen, even with a powerful microscope.

Figure 3.01

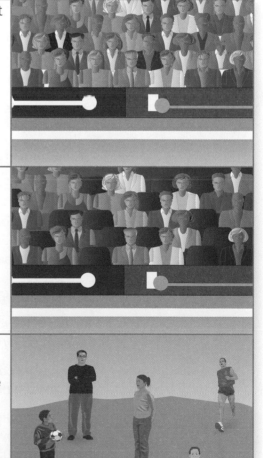

This shows a crowd in the stand at a football match. The regular arrangement of the seats means there is a pattern in the way people are arranged. If you are sitting in this stand there is little chance of moving about.
In this picture there is a crowd on the terrace. There is no regular arrangement of the people on the terrace. Although there are still a lot of people, there are gaps, so moving around is possible but not easy.
In this picture there are very few people on the grassy bank. There is no pattern in the way people are arranged on the bank. Because there are few people, it is easy to move about quickly.

These three diagrams below show the arrangement of particles in solids, liquids and gases.

It is difficult in a diagram to appreciate the different movement of the particles in solids, liquids and gases.

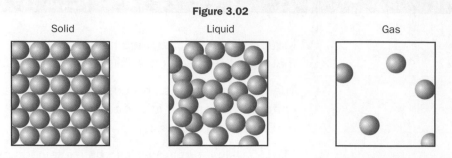

Figure 3.02

Solid   Liquid   Gas

The table compares the arrangement and movement of particles in solids, liquids and gases.

State	Arrangement of particles	Movement of particles
Solid	Particles closely packed together	Little movement – only vibrations
Liquid	Particles close together but not regularly arranged	Particles have some movement
Gas	Particles widely spaced	Particles moving rapidly in all directions

Using a particle model to explain observations

Explaining gas pressure

The particles in a gas are moving rapidly. There is no pattern to the movement. It is said to be random.

The particles hit the walls of the container. The more times the particles hit the walls, the higher the gas pressure.

If the temperature is raised, the particles move faster so there are more collisions with the walls of the container. As a result the pressure increases.

The gas is compressed into a smaller volume without changing temperature. Again, there will be more collisions with the walls. So there is an increase in pressure.

Explaining diffusion

Figure 3.03 shows two gas jars separated by a piece of card.

One gas jar contains brown bromine gas and the other contains air.

When the cardboard is removed, particles move from one jar to the other. Eventually the two gas jars contain the same mixture of bromine and air.

Figure 3.03

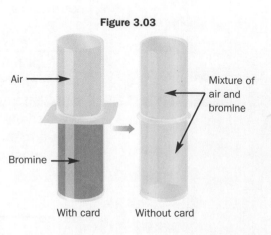

Air

Mixture of air and bromine

Bromine

With card   Without card

Explaining dissolving

If you look at the particle diagram for a liquid in Figure 3.02 you will see that there are spaces between the particles. When sugar dissolves in water the sugar particles fill the gaps between the water particles.

Explaining expansion

If a piece of steel is heated it expands. The particles in the solid vibrate more as they are heated. This vibration causes the particles to need more space and so the solid expands. A similar explanation can be used to explain the expansion of a liquid or gas.

Progress Check

1. In which state – solid, liquid or gas – are the particles most widely spaced?
2. In which state are the particles moving fastest?
3. In which state are the particles regularly arranged?
4. Why was it possible to support John Dalton's theory?

1. Gas 2. Gas 3. Solid 4. Because it supports the experimental evidence.

3.2 Atoms and elements

Learning Summary

After studying this section you should be able to:

- recognise that there are about 100 known elements
- recall the names of some elements and their symbols
- identify elements that do not fit in as either metals or non-metals

---

Elements

You will know about a large number of different materials. Materials are all made up from basic building materials called **elements**. Sometimes a material is a single element, such as gold or sulfur. Sometimes it is made up from two or more elements.

Key Point

Elements are the basic building blocks from which all materials are made. There are about 100 known elements.

The picture shows a model made of bricks. You can see that this model is made up of a number of different types of brick. Using the same bricks we could make a number of other models.

Polyester and wood are two materials with widely different properties and uses.

Figure 3.04 A model made of bricks

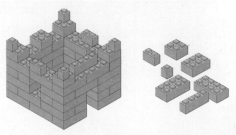

An element is broken down to the smallest part that can exist. This is called an atom. Iron is made up of iron atoms.

Both polyester and wood are made of the same three elements – carbon, hydrogen and oxygen. The elements are put together in different ways just like the bricks in different models.

Scientists use shorthand to represent the elements. Each element is given a **symbol**.

The table gives the symbols of some common elements.

Element	Symbol	Element	Symbol
Aluminium	Al	Bromine	Br
Calcium	Ca	Carbon	C
Copper	Cu	Chlorine	Cl
Iron	Fe	Fluorine	F
Lead	Pb	Helium	He
Lithium	Li	Hydrogen	H
Magnesium	Mg	Iodine	I
Potassium	K	Nitrogen	N
Silver	Ag	Oxygen	O
Sodium	Na	Phosphorus	P
Zinc	Zn	Sulfur	S

The same symbols are used by scientists throughout the world.

Classifying the elements

About 200 years ago scientists were discovering lots of new chemical elements. They attempted to find a way of grouping them. It was difficult because not all of the elements had been discovered at that time. It was like trying to complete a jigsaw without a copy of the picture and with a lot of bits missing.

In 1829 Johann Döbereiner arranged known elements into groups of three with each group having similar properties. He called these **triads**. Lithium, sodium and potassium are an example of a triad.

In 1863 John Newlands proposed his law of octaves. He placed the known elements in order of atomic mass. He then noticed that there was a similarity in the properties of every eighth element.

His ideas made some sense, but there were many errors and other scientists ridiculed him.

The breakthrough came in 1869 when the Russian schoolteacher, Dmitri Mendeleev put together the first **Periodic Table**. He arranged the known elements in order of atomic mass, but ensured that elements with similar properties were in the same column of the table.

He realised that not all the elements had been discovered and he left gaps for the missing ones. He even used his understanding to predict the properties of some of the missing elements.

Figure 3.05 shows a modern periodic table based upon the work of Mendeleev.

You do not need to remember the Periodic Table. It will be given to you in the exam when required.

The elements are shown in the **Periodic Table**. The red line divides metals on the left-hand side from non-metals on the right.

Figure 3.05

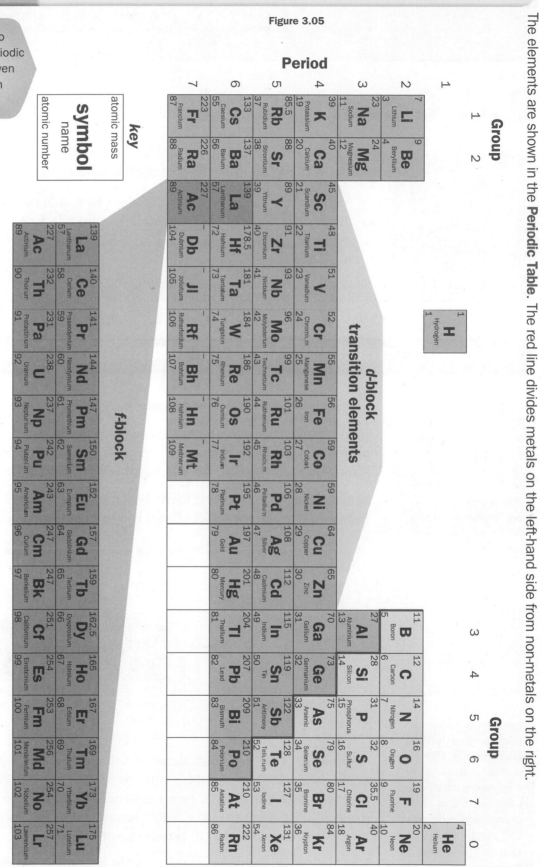

Progress Check

1. Write down the name and symbol for a non-metal in group 3 of the Periodic Table.

2. Mendeleev swapped the order of elements if it helped maintain his table. Why would he want to swap Te and I?

1. Boron (B)
2. The atomic mass of Te is greater than I, but the properties of I resemble those of Cl and Br. Note the problem is solved when atomic numbers are used.

3.3 Compounds

Learning Summary

After studying this section you should be able to:

- recall that compounds are made when elements are joined
- distinguish symbols for elements and formulae for compounds
- distinguish elements, mixtures and compounds in terms of the particles they contain
- name and describe some common mixtures

Elements combining to form compounds

You probably know that water is written as H_2O. This is called a formula and it shows us that two hydrogen atoms combine with one oxygen atom.

Certain mixtures of elements **combine** together to form **compounds**.

For example, hydrogen and oxygen are colourless gases. A mixture of hydrogen and oxygen explodes to form water (hydrogen oxide). The hydrogen and oxygen atoms join together to form liquid water.

Iron(II) sulfide is a compound formed when the elements iron and sulfur combine. The diagram shows what is happening when this reaction takes place.

Figure 3.06 The formation of iron(II) sulfide compound

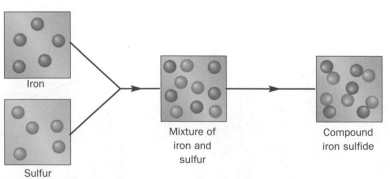

Iron

Sulfur

Mixture of iron and sulfur

Compound iron sulfide

Compounds of two elements, e.g. sodium chloride and magnesium oxide, have names ending in -ide. Compounds ending in -ate contain three elements and one of them is oxygen.

The mixture of iron and sulfur can be separated using a magnet. Iron and sulfur cannot be separated from the compound iron sulfide. When the reaction takes place and a new substance is formed, one atom of iron joins with one atom of sulfur to form one molecule of iron(II) sulfide. That is why the formula of iron(II) sulfide is written as FeS.

The table gives the names and formulae of some common compounds.

It also gives the numbers of atoms of the different elements present in the formula.

Name	Formula	Number of atoms of different elements present
Sodium chloride	NaCl	1 atom of sodium and 1 atom of chlorine
Magnesium oxide	MgO	1 atom of magnesium and 1 atom of oxygen
Calcium carbonate	$CaCO_3$	1 atom of calcium, 1 atom of carbon and 3 atoms of oxygen
Copper sulfate	$CuSO_4$	1 atom of copper, 1 atom of sulfur and 4 oxygen atoms
Sodium nitrate	$NaNO_3$	1 atom of sodium, 1 atom of nitrogen and 3 atoms of oxygen

Progress Check

1 The formula of aluminium sulfate is $Al_2(SO_4)_3$.
   (a) How many elements are there in aluminium sulfate?
   (b) How many atoms are there in one molecule of aluminium sulfate?
2 Look at the five diagrams.

1   2   3   4   5

Which diagram represents…
(a) an element?
(b) a pure compound?
(c) a mixture of elements?
(d) a mixture of compounds?
(e) a mixture of elements and compounds?

2. (a) 3 (b) 1 (c) 5 (d) 2 (e) 4
1. (a) Three (aluminium, sulfur and oxygen) (b) 17

3.4 Metals and non-metals

Learning Summary

After studying this section you should be able to:

- recall that elements can be divided into metals and non-metals
- use physical and chemical properties to classify elements as metals or non-metals

Dividing elements into metals and non-metals

If you look at the Periodic Table on page 67, you will see a red line. The line divides metals on the left hand side of the red line from non-metals on the right hand side.

But how can scientists decide whether an element is a metal or a non-metal? Sometimes an element has properties between those of a metal and those of a non-metal. An example is silicon, which looks like a metal but reacts like a non-metal. These elements are called **metalloids** or semi-metals.

Figure 3.07 gives information about the physical properties of metals and non-metals.

Figure 3.07

Metals	Non-metals
1. Usually shiny and bright; can be polished	Not shiny or bright; cannot be polished
2. Strong and tough	Not strong or tough
3. Malleable – can be made into sheets	Not malleable
4. Ductile – can be made into wire	Not ductile
5. Solids, with high melting points (e.g. iron, 1539°C; copper, 1083°C). An exception is mercury, which is a liquid at room temperature	About half are gases; the solids have low melting points (e.g. sulfur, 113°C; white phosphorus, 44°C) and low boiling points. Bromine is a liquid at room temperature
6. High density or relative density (e.g. mercury, lead)	Low density (e.g. most are gases; white phosphorus)
7. Good conductors of heat and electricity	Poor conductors of heat and electricity
8. Ring or make a sound when hit, e.g. a school bell	Do not ring when hit

There are many exceptions to this list. For example:
- Mercury is a liquid metal (melting point is –39°C).
- Sodium and potassium (metals) have densities so low that they float on water (density of sodium 0.97g/cm^3, density of potassium 0.86g/cm^3). Their melting points are also low (sodium 97°C, potassium 62°C) and they are so soft that they can easily be cut with a knife.
- Carbon (non-metal) has a high melting point (about 3500°C). In the form called graphite it is a shiny solid and a good conductor of electricity.

An element is called a metal if it has most, but not necessarily all, of the metallic properties in the table above. A better way of deciding if an element is a metal or non-metal is to use chemical properties.

Figure 3.08 shows the combustion of an element in a gas jar filled with oxygen gas or air. The product is an **oxide** of the element.

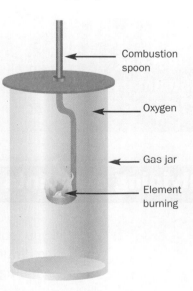

Combustion spoon

Oxygen

Gas jar

Element burning

Figure 3.08

Figure 3.09 shows the results of burning five elements in air and oxygen.

Figure 3.09

Element	Combustion in air	Combustion in oxygen	pH of residue	Name of residue
Magnesium	Burns brightly with a white flame	Burns brightly with a white flame	11 (strongly basic)	Magnesium oxide
Sulfur	Burns with a very small blue flame	Burns with a bigger blue flame	4 (acidic)	Sulfur dioxide
Copper	No noticeable flame. Copper glows red hot		7 (neutral)	Coating of copper oxide
Carbon	Glows red	Glows brighter	5.5 (slightly acidic)	Carbon dioxide
Iron	Glows red	Burns well	7 (neutral)	Iron oxide

The results of this experiment show the following:

1 Elements burn better in oxygen than in air.

2 Metals burn to form neutral or basic oxides.

3 Non-metals burn to form acidic oxides.

Metals have other chemical properties that might help in their classification, e.g. they often react with an acid to form hydrogen. For example:

magnesium + sulfuric acid ⟶ magnesium sulfate + hydrogen

Progress Check

1 The table shows the results of burning three elements P, Q and R in oxygen. (Note: P, Q and R are not their chemical symbols).
Classify each element as a metal or a non-metal.

Element	Burn in oxygen	pH of residue
P	Small flame	7
Q	Yellow flame	3
R	Glows red	8

2 Use the Periodic Table on page 67 to classify each of these elements as a metal or a non-metal.
Sr   Se   Co   F

1. P – metal; Q – non-metal; R – metal.
2. Metals – Sr and Co, Non-metals – Se and F

3.5 Acids and bases

Learning Summary

After studying this section you should be able to:

- name some common acids and bases
- recall that solutions can be classified as acidic, basic or neutral using indicators
- understand the pH scale and recall what happens to pH when a substance is neutralised
- know some everyday uses of acids, bases and neutralisation

What are acids and bases?

The acids you use will probably look like water as they are mixed with water or diluted before use. Never assume that a colourless liquid is water.

Many substances in the world around us are acids or bases. The sharp taste we get when we bite into an apple is an acid. Acids always have a sour taste although we would be very unwise to taste most of them!

Acids are found in lemons, oranges and limes. These are called citrus fruits and the acid is citric acid. The sourness of vinegar is caused by the acid it contains. This is called ethanoic acid. There are three common acids we use in the laboratory. They are sometimes called mineral acids. They are:

- Sulfuric acid H_2SO_4
- Nitric acid HNO_3
- Hydrochloric acid HCl

Bases are in some ways the opposite of acids. They will react with and 'cancel out' acids. Common bases in the home are found in bicarbonate of soda, washing powders and washing soda. Common bases in the laboratory include:

- Sodium hydroxide $NaOH$ (sometimes called caustic soda)
- Potassium hydroxide KOH
- Calcium hydroxide $Ca(OH)_2$
- Ammonia NH_3

Substances, such as water, that are neither acidic nor basic are said to be **neutral**.

Progress Check

1. Write down the names of five acids.
2. Write down the names of five bases.
3. All acids are made up of different elements. Sulfuric acid is made up from hydrogen, sulfur and oxygen. Which elements make up nitric acid and hydrochloric acid?
4. Which element is present in all acids?

4. Hydrogen
3. Nitric acid – hydrogen, nitrogen and oxygen. Hydrochloric acid – hydrogen and chlorine.
2. Bicarbonate of soda, washing soda, washing powders, sodium hydroxide, potassium hydroxide, calcium hydroxide, ammonia.
1. Citric acid, ethanoic acid, sulfuric acid, nitric acid, hydrochloric acid.

Detecting acids and bases

Figure 3.10 Which test tube contains a base?

A   B

Acids and bases can be detected using coloured solutions obtained from plants. These coloured substances change colour when added to acids and bases. They are called indicators.

If some red colour is extracted from red cabbage it can be used as an indicator. If the red cabbage solution is added to an acid, the solution stays red. If it is added to a base it turns green.

Other extracts from plants can be used. Litmus is a purple-coloured extract from a lichen or moss. If **litmus** is added to an acid, the solution turns red. If it is added to a base, the solution turns blue.

Sometimes scientists use a piece of paper soaked in litmus. They call this litmus paper. It is easier than carrying bottles of liquid.

Key Point	Acid	Base	
	Red	**Blue**	when litmus is the indicator

Progress Check

1. What colour is litmus in a neutral solution?
   (Hint: Think of neutral as being halfway between acid and base.)
2. Three test tubes contain different liquids. A piece of red litmus paper and a piece of blue litmus paper are added to each tube. The results are:

Liquid	Red litmus	Blue litmus
A	stays red	turns red
B	turns blue	stays blue
C	stays red	stays blue

What can you conclude about each liquid from these tests?

1. Purple 2. A – acid; B – base; C – neutral.

Litmus paper and similar indicators are useful for detecting acids and bases but they do not compare their different strengths. **Universal Indicator** is better. It is a mixture of simple indicators and it changes through a series of different colours. The pH value can be found from the colour.

The pH value is a number on a scale from 0 to 14 which shows how acidic or how basic a substance is. The indicator shows a different colour for different **pH values**.

If Universal Indicator solution is added to a solution and the solution turns orange, the pH value is 5 and the substance is a weak acid.

Figure 3.11 The colours for a simple form of Universal Indicator

	pH	Colour of Universal Indicator	Example in the home	Examples in the laboratory
Strong acids	1		Car battery acid	Mineral acids
	2			
	3	red		
Weak acids	4		Lemon juice, vinegar	Carbonic acid
	5	orange		
	6	yellow	Soda water	
Neutral	7	green	Water, salt, ethanol	Sodium hydrogencarbonate
Weak bases	8	blue	Soap, baking powder	
	9	blue/purple		
	10			Ammonia solution
Strong bases	11		Washing soda	
	12	purple	Oven cleaner	
	13			Sodium and potassium hydroxides
	14			

Progress Check

1. What is the pH value of a neutral solution?
2. What colour does Universal Indicator turn in a solution of pH value 9?
3. What pH value has a solution that turns Universal Indicator yellow?
4. Two solutions are tested with Universal Indicator. Solution X goes red and solution Y turns yellow. Which is the stronger acid?

1. 7 2. Blue/purple 3. 6 4. X

Scientists wanting to make a number of pH readings may use a **pH meter**. This consists of a glass probe attached to a meter. A reading can be made or pH values transferred to a computer.

Figure 3.12 A pH meter being used to measure the pH of a solution.

Neutralisation

When a base is added to an acid, the pH value changes. The graph shows the changes when sodium hydroxide is added to hydrochloric acid. A pH meter is used to follow changes in pH.

The effects of the acid are cancelled out by the base. This change is called **neutralisation**.

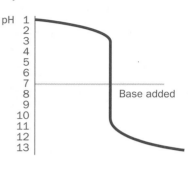

Figure 3.13 Graph showing changes in pH

Examples of neutralisation

1 Everyone has several hundred cubic centimetres of hydrochloric acid in the gastric juices of the stomach. This acid is used in the digestion of food. Minor problems of indigestion can be caused by excess acid in the stomach. This excess acid can be neutralised by adding a weak base, called an antacid. Suitable antacids are milk of magnesia (a suspension of magnesium hydroxide) and bicarbonate of soda (sodium hydrogencarbonate).

2 Farmers have to control the pH values of their soil. If the soil becomes too acidic, a good yield of crops cannot be grown. Rain and artificial fertilisers make the soil more acidic. The farmer can neutralise the excess acidity by treating the soil with lime (calcium hydroxide).

Progress Check

1 If some sulfuric acid is spilt onto the floor, bicarbonate of soda is added. Why is this done?
2 A wasp sting is treated with vinegar but a bee sting is treated with bicarbonate of soda. Suggest why different treatments are given.
3 Inland lakes can become too acidic for fish to live in. What can be added to the lake to neutralise the water?

1. To neutralise the acid.   2. Wasp sting contains base so needs an acid to neutralise it. Bee sting contains an acid so needs a base to neutralise it.   3. Lime

Assessment questions

1. The table gives some information about four substances.

Substance	Melting point (°C)	Conductor of electricity	Appearance
Sulfur	114	No	Yellow solid
Paraffin wax	50–70	No	White solid
Mercury	-39	Yes	Silver liquid
Oxygen	-218	No	Colourless gas

(a) What information in the table suggests that mercury is a metal?

_____

_____ [2]

(b) What information in the table suggests that paraffin wax is a mixture of substances but the other substances are pure?

_____

_____ [2]

(c) About two hundred years ago the French scientist, Lavoisier, found that a red solid was formed when mercury and oxygen were heated together.

(i) Choose the word from the list that best describes the red solid.

compound   **element**   **mixture**

_____ [1]

(ii) Give a chemical name for the red solid.

_____ [1]

2. Sam spills some dilute acid on the bench. What should she do to clear it up safely? Tick the correct box.

Leave it to dry completely	
Add some water and leave it to dry	
Add bicarbonate of soda and wash with water	
Set it alight and let it burn	

[1]

Assessment questions

3. The table gives the properties of five elements **A–E**. (Note: These letters are **not** their chemical symbols.)

Element	Melting point (˚C)	Appearance	Conductor of electricity	pH of oxide
A	114	Dull	No	4
B	327	Dull	Yes	7
C	3720	Dull	Yes	5
D	1063	Shiny	Yes	7
E	-39	Shiny	No	7

Which elements are metals and which are non-metals?

_____

_____ **[2]**

4. The table shows part of the modern Periodic Table. In this table, elements that are solids at room temperature are printed in black, elements that are liquid are printed in blue and elements that are gases are printed in red.

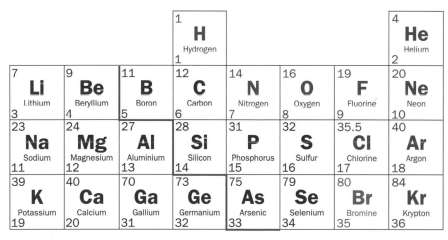

Which of the following statements are true and which are false?

A There are more metals in the table than liquids.

B The gases are towards the right and top of the table.

C Lithium, sodium and potassium have similar properties.

D Phosphorus, sulfur and chlorine are in the same group.

E All elements with single letter symbols are gases.

True: _____ False: _____ **[3]**

Assessment questions

5.   The table shows results obtained when zinc oxide and zinc carbonate are heated in separate test tubes.

	Appearance before heating	Appearance after heating	Mass before heating (g)	Mass after heating (g)
Zinc oxide	White powder	Turns yellow but turns white again on cooling	2.3g	2.3g
Zinc carbonate	White powder	Turns yellow but turns white again on cooling	2.3g	2.0g

(a)   Give reasons why the information suggests zinc carbonate is split up but zinc oxide is not.

_____

_____ [2]

(b)   Finish the word equation

Zinc carbonate ⟶ _____ + _____ [2]

Levels 7–8

6.   Sodium hydrogencarbonate has the formula $NaHCO_3$

(a)   How many different elements are there combined in sodium hydrogencarbonate?

_____

_____ [1]

(b)   How many atoms are there of each element?

_____

_____ [1]

(c)   What is the total number of atoms in the formula?

_____

_____ [1]

Assessment questions

7. Ali heats up a sample of a solid acid in a boiling tube until all the acid has melted. He then allows the boiling tube and contents to cool whilst recording the temperature every minute.

The graph below shows his results.

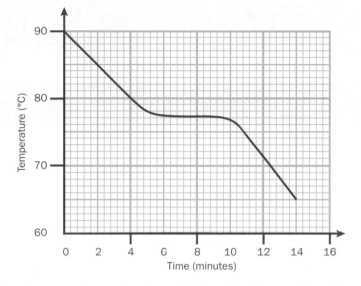

Describe fully the changes that take place during 14 minutes. Use ideas about particles in your answer.

_____

_____

_____

_____

_____

_____

_____

_____

_____ **[6]**

4 Energy, electricity and forces

			Studied	Revised	Assessment questions
4.1	**Energy**	– Energy transfer – Energy flow			
4.2	**Energy resources**	– Fuels and energy – Renewable resources – Fuel cells – Measuring energy			
4.3	**Light energy**	– How light travels – Seeing – Mirrors – Light changing speed and direction			
4.4	**Sound energy**	– Sound production – Travelling sound – Hearing			
4.5	**Forces and their effects**	– What do forces do? – Staying still – Floating and sinking – Getting moving – Resistive forces			
4.6	**Speeding up**	– Who won the race? – How long does it take? – Using graphs			
4.7	**Pressure and moments**	– Under pressure – Quantifying pressure – Turning forces – A question of balance			
4.8	**Electricity**	– Currents in circuits – Different types of circuit – Controlling the current – Measuring voltage – Measuring current – Changing the current – Some effects of an electric current			

4.1 Energy

Energy transfer

Questions in Key Stage 3 tests often ask you to identify the type of energy that an object has, for example kinetic energy or gravitational potential energy.

Every event involves **energy** and an **energy transfer**. Devices that we use in our everyday living transfer energy. The diagrams show some examples.

The kettle transfers energy from **electricity** to **heat** in the water.	
The solar cell in this calculator transfers energy from **light** into **electricity**.	
The loudspeaker transfers energy from **electricity** to **sound**, which is **kinetic energy** of the air particles.	
The ski lift transfers energy from **electricity** to **gravitational potential energy** of the people as they are lifted up.	
As the bus speeds up, **chemical energy** stored in the fuel is transferred to **movement** or **kinetic energy** and heat in the exhaust gases, and some sound energy.	

Gravitational potential energy is sometimes referred to as just 'potential energy'.

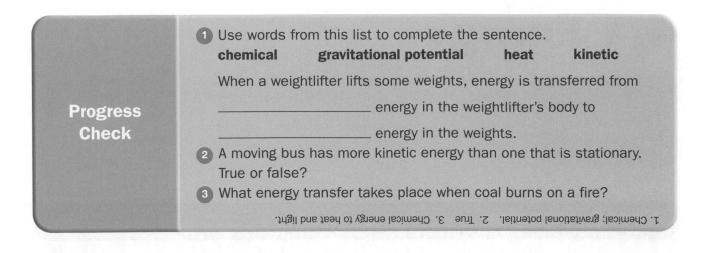

Progress Check

1. Use words from this list to complete the sentence.

   chemical   gravitational potential   heat   kinetic

   When a weightlifter lifts some weights, energy is transferred from _____ energy in the weightlifter's body to _____ energy in the weights.
2. A moving bus has more kinetic energy than one that is stationary. True or false?
3. What energy transfer takes place when coal burns on a fire?

1. Chemical; gravitational potential.   2. True   3. Chemical energy to heat and light.

Energy flow

The lamp is not gaining any energy because it operates at a constant temperature.

Figure 4.01

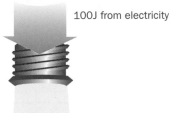

100J from electricity

95J as heat and infra-red radiation

5J as light

When a kettle is used to heat some water, the kettle and its contents are gaining energy as they warm up.

When a lamp is used to light a room, energy **flows** through the lamp at a constant rate. The diagram shows the energy flow through the lamp each second.

All the energy that flows into the lamp also flows out – this is known as **conservation of energy**.

Key Point

Energy is never created or destroyed – this is the principle of conservation of energy.

Do not confuse this with 'conserving energy resources', which means taking action to make our fossil fuel supplies last longer.

The temperature rise is so small, it would be very difficult to detect with a thermometer.

If you turn off a light at the mains switch, the room goes dark immediately. Light doesn't stay as light for very long after leaving the lamp, so the light in a room has to be continually replaced. What happens to the energy that leaves the lamp?

- The hot lamp loses energy to the surrounding air – this is carried away by a convection current.
- The light and infra-red radiation are absorbed by the walls and other surfaces – causing them to warm up.

The effect is that all the energy from the lamp is spread out or **dissipated** in the room, causing a very small temperature rise.

Almost all the energy that we take from sources such as electricity, gas, coal and petrol ends up as heat in our surroundings – in the buildings that we live in, the air and the outdoors. We cannot get this energy back very easily; it is much easier to obtain more energy from a fuel or electricity than to extract the energy from the air and the ground outside.

Progress Check

1. Explain why it is not possible to obtain more energy out of an appliance than the amount that goes in.
2. Complete the sentence:

   When energy spreads out it is said to be ____________________ .
3. Almost all the energy transferred from electricity ends up as heat. True or false?

1. Energy is always conserved – it cannot be made. 2. dissipated 3. True

4.2 Energy resources

Learning Summary

After studying this section you should be able to:

- understand how energy can be released from a fuel
- describe how renewable energy resources can be used for heating and to generate electricity
- explain why it is important to conserve fossil fuels
- identify and describe some energy transfers

Fuels and energy

Even sitting doing nothing needs energy to keep our hearts pumping blood around our bodies.

An energy resource is a supply of energy.

Whatever we do needs **energy**. Energy is needed to:

- make things **move**
- **heat** our living space
- **light** the areas where we live and work

Electricity provides much of the energy that we need each day. The diagrams show examples of electricity being used to produce heat, light and movement.

Figure 4.02

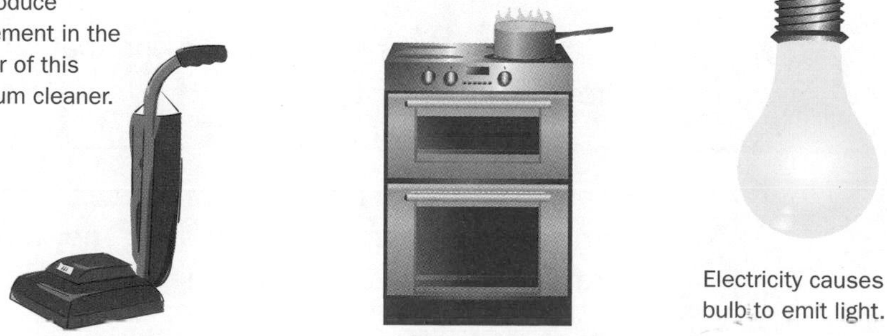
Electricity is used to produce movement in the motor of this vacuum cleaner.
Electricity is used to heat this pan of water.
Electricity causes this bulb to emit light.

Some modern power stations generate electricity by burning wood from fast-growing willow trees.

Most of our electricity is generated by burning a **fuel**. A fuel is something that burns in air and releases heat. Common fuels include wood, gas, coal and oil. Of these, wood is easy to replace as more trees can be grown. Coal, oil and natural gas are **fossil fuels** – they took millions of years to form and cannot be replaced.

It is important to remember that all the energy stored in coal, oil and natural gas originally came from the Sun.

Coal was formed from giant fern-like plants. They trapped energy from the Sun as they grew. In time the decaying remains of these plants became covered in mud, sand and clay. Over millions of years the pressure from above, together with heat from the Earth below, caused coal to form from the remains of the ferns.

Oil and natural gas formed in a similar way, but from animals rather than plants. When animals that live in the sea die, their remains form layers on the seabed. The combined effects of pressure and heat over millions of years resulted in oil and gas.

Fossil fuels are being used up rapidly.
- The UK has enough coal to last for 200 years.
- A lot of this coal will be expensive to recover from the ground.
- The known reserves of gas and oil will not last as long as coal, but new reserves are being found every year.
- Our use of gas, oil and coal needs to be as efficient as possible so as not to waste these fuels.
- We need to find alternative sources of energy for transport and for generating electricity.

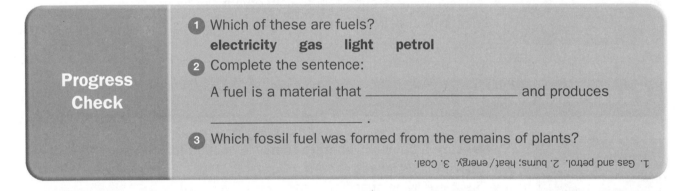

Progress Check

1. Which of these are fuels?
   electricity   gas   light   petrol
2. Complete the sentence:
   A fuel is a material that _____ and produces
   _____ .
3. Which fossil fuel was formed from the remains of plants?

1. Gas and petrol. 2. burns; heat / energy. 3. Coal.

Renewable resources

We will always need to heat and light our homes and to have energy for transport. Fossil fuels will not last for ever, so we have to develop the use of renewable energy resources.

Key Point

A renewable energy resource is one that will not run out during the lifetime of the Earth.

A common error at Key Stage 3 is to describe a renewable resource as one that can be re-used over and over again. Wood can only be burned once!

Plants are renewable energy resources that provide food, which in turn provides the energy for our bodies. They are renewable because we can grow fresh crops each year. Energy from plants is known as **biomass**.

Other renewable resources include:
- wind
- waves and tides
- moving water
- the Sun
- geothermal energy

Figure 4.03 A wind farm

Hemera / Thinkstock

Energy from the Sun makes the **wind** blow. The energy in moving air has been used for thousands of years to turn windmills.

Recently in the UK there has been a large increase in the number of wind turbines that generate electricity. These can be built singly or in groups, called wind farms.

In some areas of the country the wind blows all the time. There are now plans to build wind farms off the east coast, so that people are not affected by the noise that they make.

> The Sun also has some effect on the tides. Very high tides are caused by the Sun and the Moon pulling together.

The sea provides two important energy resources: **waves** and **tides**.

Waves are caused by the wind, and tides are due mainly to the effect of the Moon pulling on the oceans. Attempts to extract energy from the waves have proved costly and unreliable, as the equipment has been damaged in storms.

Energy from tides has been used for hundreds of years to drive mills. It is predictable and reliable, as it depends only on the Moon orbiting the Earth. In the UK there are no power stations driven by tides, but the one on the estuary of the river La Rance in France generates enough electricity to supply a large town.

In Scotland and Wales there are fast-flowing streams and rivers that are used to generate electricity from **moving water**. The water passes through a **turbine**, which drives a **generator**. The energy source here is the Sun, which causes the evaporation of water from the sea. This water vapour forms clouds and falls as rain.

> Most of our energy comes from the Sun. The exceptions are energy from the tides, which comes mainly from the Moon, and geothermal energy.

Energy from the Sun is used directly in three different ways:

- It is used to grow crops.
- It can be used to heat water.
- It can be used to generate electricity.

In countries with more sunshine than in the UK, hot water tanks on the roofs of houses are a common sight. Energy from the Sun is used to heat water as it passes through copper pipes. These pipes are painted black to absorb as much radiant energy as possible.

Solar cells use energy from the Sun to produce electricity. They are expensive to make so the cost of the electricity from them is high. Another disadvantage is that they only produce electricity in daylight. They are useful to power calculators, which only use a small amount of electricity. They can also be much cheaper to install than mains electricity in remote places. In some countries they provide the electricity for telephones. A battery is used to store electricity generated during the day so that the telephones can be used at night.

Figure 4.04 This traffic light uses solar cells to provide the electricity that it needs

iStockphoto / Thinkstock

Solar cells are used by satellites and spacecraft to generate electricity. They have vast panels of cells to generate enough electricity for the on-board computers and other devices. They also store the energy in batteries so that they have a reserve supply.

Geothermal energy is the energy in hot rocks below the Earth's surface. The energy in the rocks is used to heat water. If the rocks are hot enough, they can be used to generate steam to drive a turbine and produce electricity.

Fuel cells

Combustion of hydrogen releases energy, but is not very efficient.

$$\text{Hydrogen} + \text{oxygen} \longrightarrow \text{water} + \text{energy}$$

This change occurs with 100% efficiency in a fuel cell.

Streams of hydrogen and oxygen enter the **fuel cell** and are converted into water and useful energy including electricity. Figure 4.05 shows a diagram of a hydrogen-oxygen fuel cell.

Fuel cells are seen as a possible way of powering cars and other vehicles in the future. They provide the energy to power an electric motor without producing damaging pollutants.

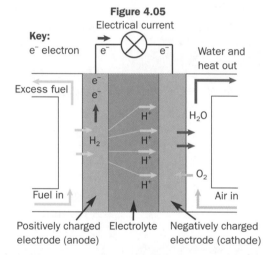

Figure 4.05

Measuring energy

When a gas or electricity bill arrives at home, the cost is for the energy transferred through the gas pipes or electricity cables.

One **joule** of energy is a very small amount. It is the amount of energy that leaves your body when you lift a 1kg bag of sugar through a height of 1 metre.

Key Point	Energy is measured in joules (J).

To boil a kettle of water from cold needs about 600000J of energy, so you can imagine that a lot of energy is needed to heat enough water to fill a bath.

Progress Check

1. Wood is renewable because it can be re-used. True or false?
2. What name is given to energy obtained from hot underground rocks?
3. Most of the energy used to boil a kettle of water comes from fossil fuels. True or false?
4. If it takes 10J of energy to lift a 1kg weight to a height of 1m, how much energy is needed to lift a 25kg sack of potatoes a vertical distance of 3m?

1. False 2. Geothermal energy. 3. True 4. 750J

4.3 Light energy

Learning Summary

After studying this section you should be able to:

- understand how light travels and how objects are seen
- describe how light is reflected at a mirror
- recall the change in direction when light changes speed at a boundary

How light travels

Sharp shadows are formed when **light** from a small source, such as a torch, passes around an object that is **opaque**, i.e. that does not let light go through it.

Key Point These shadows provide evidence that light travels in straight lines.

If a low-flying aircraft passes overhead, when you look at where the sound is coming from you see that the aircraft has already gone past. This is because of the different speeds of light and sound.

Key Point Light travels very much faster than sound.

Typical speeds, in air, are:
- sound – 330m/s
- light – 300 000 000m/s

Because of the very fast speed of light, there is normally no noticeable time delay between an event happening and us seeing it.

Never look directly at the Sun, as it could damage your eyes.

Exceptions to this occur when the distances are vast, for example when looking at stars. Observations of our Sun see what happened eight and a half minutes ago.

Light from the second nearest star to us, Proxima Centauri, takes more than four years to get here, so when you are star-gazing you are looking back in time!

Seeing

Some people think that we see just with our eyes, but we also need a brain to be able to see things!
- Eyes are sensors that send messages to the brain along the optic nerve in the form of electrical signals.
- When the brain interprets the signals from the eyes, it assumes that the light travelled to the eyes in a straight line.

- This enables the brain to work out where things are.
- The brain needs light from both eyes to be able to pinpoint the position of objects accurately, as the diagram shows.

Figure 4.06

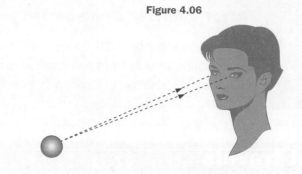

The difference between how we see luminous and non-luminous objects is frequently tested at Key Stage 3.

Television and computer screens are **luminous**: they give out light that our eyes detect. Lamps and the Sun also give out light, as do fires and candles.

We use light sources, such as the Sun and artificial lighting, so that we can see other things. Most surfaces **scatter** light, that is they **reflect** it in all directions, so that some light enters your eyes even when you move to a different position.

Progress Check

1 Complete the sentence:

A luminous object gives out _____ , but a

non-luminous object only _____ it.

2 We see an event before we hear the sound from it because light travels faster than sound. True or false?

3 Imagine you are sitting in a chair after dark, using a reading lamp to help you to read a book. Describe how you can see the book.

3. Light from the book is scattered (reflected in all directions). Some of it passes into the eyes.

1. light; reflects   2. True

Mirrors

Unlike most everyday things, mirrors do not reflect light in all directions, but they do reflect it in a regular and predictable way.

Key Point

Light is reflected from a mirror at the same angle as it hits it.

Figure 4.07

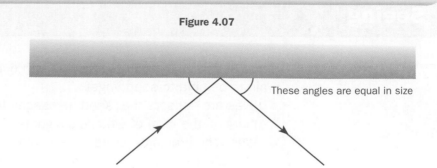

These angles are equal in size

A common misconception is that the image in a mirror is 'laterally inverted' or turned round sideways. It isn't. When you look into a mirror, you see the image of the left side of your face on your left.

We use this regular reflection when we look at our image in a mirror. Looking into a mirror causes our brain to get confused: it 'sees' things that aren't really there!

● Light from your nose (and other parts of you!) hits the mirror and is reflected at equal angles. The reflected light is detected by your eyes.

● Your brain then 'sees' the nose, and works out where it is, assuming that the light has travelled in straight lines.

● In this case it gets things wrong: it 'sees' a nose behind the mirror.

Figure 4.08

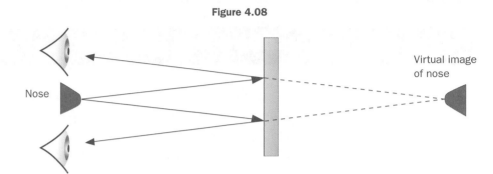

The dotted lines show where light does not actually travel, but only appears to come from.

What you see is called a **virtual image**. The word 'image' just means 'likeness', and in all respects the image is a likeness of the real thing; it is the same way up and the same size and colour. The image is called virtual because, unlike the image that you see on a television or cinema screen, it is not really there.

Using the rule about the way in which light is reflected at a mirror, you can construct images.

Key Point

The image in a mirror is always formed straight behind the mirror, the same distance behind it as the object is in front of the mirror.

Many pupils at this level think that the image is actually on the mirror, rather than behind it.

Mirrors are used in periscopes to turn light round corners. Light hitting a mirror at an angle of 45° is reflected at the same angle and so is effectively turned through 90°. The diagram shows how two mirrors are arranged inside a periscope. You can make a periscope quite easily using two small mirror tiles and the cardboard tube from the inside of a roll of kitchen foil.

Figure 4.09 Two mirrors arranged to make a periscope

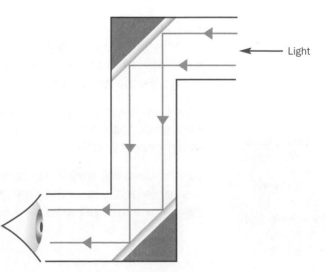

Progress Check

1. When you look in a mirror, is the image that you see real or virtual?
2. Which is correct – **A**, **B** or **C**?
   A The image in a mirror is further from the mirror than the object is.
   B The image in a mirror is closer to the mirror than the object is.
   C The image in a mirror is the same distance away as the object is.

1. Virtual 2. C

Light changing speed and direction

Have you ever noticed how the water in a swimming pool never looks to be as deep as it says it is? This is another example of your eye-brain system being fooled when light does not travel in straight lines. A **change in the speed** at which light travels can also cause a **change in direction**.

As light enters water or any other dense transparent material it slows down.

Typical speeds of light in water and glass are:
- water – 230 000 000 m/s
- glass – 200 000 000 m/s

The change in speed of light as it enters water or glass is called **refraction**. The diagrams show the effect of the change in speed when light passes through a sheet of glass.

Figure 4.10

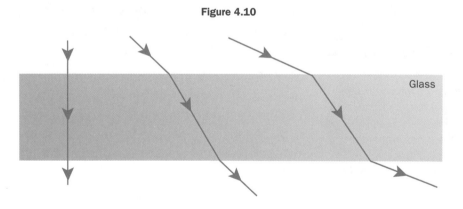

> The greater the angle at which the light meets the air-glass boundary, the greater the change in direction.

- The light that meets the air/glass boundary at an angle of 90° carries on without a change in direction.
- At any other angle the light changes direction as it goes into and leaves the glass block.

Light travelling through water undergoes a similar change in direction. The amount of change is slightly less because there is less change in speed as light enters water.

> When viewed through water, objects only appear to about three-quarters of their real distance away.

So why does the swimming pool look to be shallower than it really is? The answer is because of the change in direction that occurs when light leaves the water and speeds up as it enters the air.

Figure 4.11 If you drop a coin into a swimming pool, the image appears closer than it really is

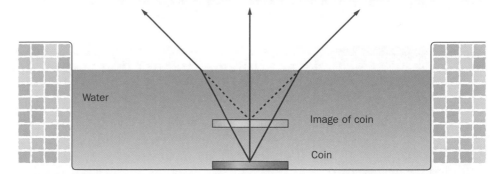

The dotted lines in the diagram show where the light appears to have come from, assuming that it has travelled in straight lines. This is another example of a **virtual image**. As with a mirror, the virtual image is just like the original object, except that it is not really there.

Progress Check

1 Complete the sentence:
When light passes from air into glass it slows down. This effect is called _____ .

2 The bottom of a swimming pool appears to be closer than it really is. True or false?

3 The diagram shows light from a lamp passing through a block of glass.

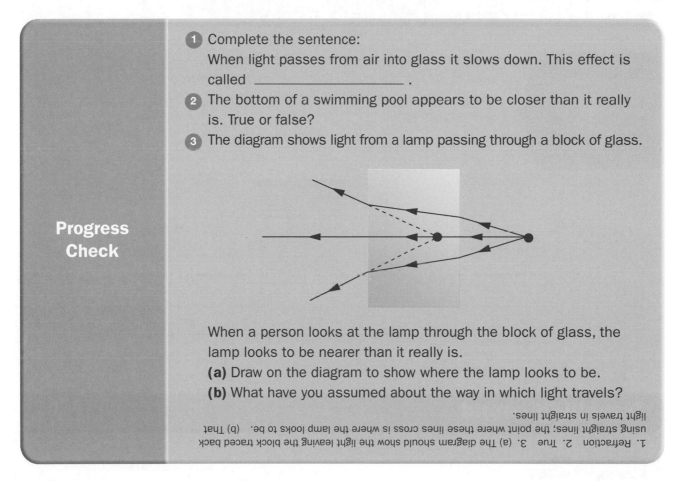

When a person looks at the lamp through the block of glass, the lamp looks to be nearer than it really is.

(a) Draw on the diagram to show where the lamp looks to be.

(b) What have you assumed about the way in which light travels?

1. Refraction   2. True   3. (a) The diagram should show the light leaving the block traced back using straight lines; the point where these lines cross is where the lamp looks to be.   (b) That light travels in straight lines.

4.4 Sound energy

Learning Summary

After studying this section you should be able to:

● describe how sound is produced
● explain how changing the amplitude and frequency of a sound changes the sound that is heard
● describe how sound is detected by an ear
● explain why ears need to be protected from loud sounds and how this is done

Sound production

When answering questions about what causes sound, always stress that sound is caused by an object vibrating.

To make a **sound**, something has to **vibrate** in a to-and-fro motion. Televisions, radios and hi-fi all use **loudspeakers** to reproduce sound. A loudspeaker consists of a paper cone driven backwards and forwards by an electromagnet.

Figure 4.12 A loudspeaker

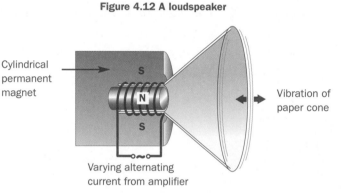

Cylindrical permanent magnet

Vibration of paper cone

Varying alternating current from amplifier

Some musical instruments have strings that vibrate when they are hit or plucked; others have columns of air that vibrate when they are blown.

Travelling sound

Sound travels slowest in gases because the particles are the most widespread.

Sound can travel through anything that has particles capable of transmitting the vibrations.

It travels very fast in solids, where the particles are close together, slower in liquids and slowest of all in gases.

Key Point

Sound cannot travel in a vacuum – it needs a material to transmit the sound by vibrations of its particles.

You may have seen a demonstration of a bell ringing inside a glass jar. Sound from the bell travels through the air and the glass and then air again to the ear. When air is removed from the jar, the sound cannot be heard.

A **slinky spring** can be used to show how sound waves travel through materials. As the wave moves along the spring, each part of the spring vibrates. The particles in air vibrate in a similar way when they transmit sound. Each wave consists of a **compression** or squash, where the particles are close together, followed by a **rarefaction** or stretch, where the particles are further apart.

Figure 4.13

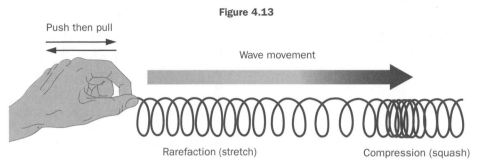

Push then pull

Wave movement

Rarefaction (stretch)   Compression (squash)

A hand pushing and pulling a slinky spring is a good model of what happens when a loudspeaker cone is pushing and pulling on the air.

- Using this model, **moving the hand further** has the same effect on the spring as **turning up the volume control** has on the air particles.
- The particles **move further** and you hear a **louder** sound.
- When you push further you are increasing the **amplitude** of the vibration.

Key Point

The amplitude of the vibration is the greatest distance that each part of the slinky moves from its rest position.

A microphone and an oscilloscope can be used to plot a graph that shows the movement of air particles when a sound wave passes. The upwards and downwards movement of the oscilloscope trace represents the forwards and backwards movement of an air particle.

The distance marked with an arrow (Figure 4.14) represents the amplitude of the wave. A louder sound of the **same pitch** has a larger amplitude.

The trace on an oscilloscope screen shows the number of sound waves that are detected in a certain time; the actual time can be changed by adjusting the oscilloscope settings. A 'crest' and a 'trough' show one complete wave. The trace shown in the diagram below shows two and a half waves.

Figure 4.14 An oscilloscope trace of two and a half waves

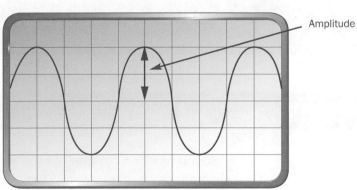

Amplitude

Make sure that you know how amplitude and frequency are shown by the trace on an oscilloscope screen. Questions about this are common at Key Stage 3.

The next diagram shows the trace when a note of higher pitch is played.

Figure 4.15 A trace of a higher pitched note

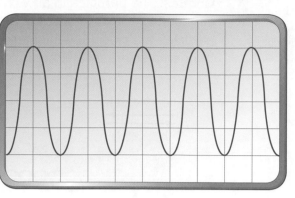

There are now more waves in the same time; the frequency (the number of waves per second) has increased.

Key Point

Frequency is measured in hertz (Hz). 1Hz = 1 wave per second.

These measurements using an oscilloscope display show that:
● increasing the **amplitude** of a sound wave makes it sound louder
● increasing the **frequency** of a sound wave gives it a higher pitch

Progress Check

1 Complete the sentence:

All sounds are caused by _____ .

2 Sound can only travel in solids. True or false?

3 Choose the correct word from the list to complete the sentence.

Frequency is measured in _____ .

amps   hertz   metres   seconds

4 You can make a sound by plucking a stretched rubber band.

(a) How does the rubber band make a sound when it is plucked?

(b) Describe how the sound is carried from the rubber band to your ears.

(c) How does the sound change if the rubber band is plucked harder? What causes this change?

(d) If the rubber band is stretched more, when it is plucked the sound has a higher pitch. What change has caused the higher pitch?

1. Vibrations.   2. False.   3. Hertz.   4. (a) By vibrating.   (b) By vibrations of the air particles.   (c) It sounds louder. The vibrations have a greater amplitude.   (d) There are more vibrations each second or the frequency has increased.

Hearing

Sound reaches our ears as the energy of vibrating air particles. The vibrations have a tiny amplitude, typically a few thousandths of a millimetre, but our ears are very sensitive to small amounts of energy transmitted in this way.

Figure 4.16 The ear

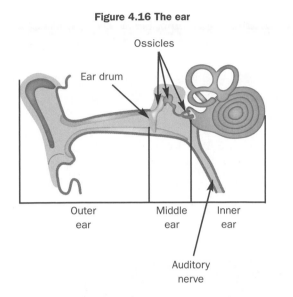

Ossicles

Ear drum

Outer
ear

Middle
ear

Inner
ear

Auditory
nerve

In an ear:

- sound causes vibrations of the ear drum in the outer ear
- the ossicles are three bones in the middle ear that transfer this energy to the inner ear
- **nerve endings** in the inner ear are stimulated by the vibration and send messages along the auditory nerve to the brain. These messages are sent as electrical impulses.

Not everybody can hear the same sounds.

- The ears of a normal young person detect sounds with a frequency ranging from about 20Hz to about 20000Hz.
- As you get older, the range of frequencies that you can hear is reduced.
- A middle-aged person may not be able to hear sounds with a frequency greater than 15000Hz although the hearing at low frequencies is less likely to be affected.
- Even within this range, your ears are more sensitive to some frequencies than to others, sounds at a frequency of around 2000Hz sounding louder than higher or lower sounds.

> Small animals communicate using higher frequencies than those used by large animals.

Other animals have different frequency ranges. Bats can emit and detect sound waves that are well above the range of human hearing, and dog whistles use a high frequency that humans cannot hear. Elephants and dolphins can communicate over long distances using very low frequencies that have a longer distance range than high frequency waves.

People who work in noisy environments should wear ear muffs to protect their ears from damage. Sudden exposure to a loud sound, such as an explosion, can cause immediate damage by breaking the ear drum or the ossicles.

The ossicles are also subject to wear; they are pieces of machinery in constant use. A person who is repeatedly subjected to loud sounds, such as those from pneumatic drills or discos, suffers loss of hearing as the ossicles wear away. Surgeons can sometimes replace worn out ossicles with plastic ones to improve a person's hearing.

Progress Check

1. Which two frequencies of sound waves cannot be detected by most humans?
   10Hz   35Hz   1000Hz   15000Hz   25000Hz
2. Disc jockeys and pop singers often suffer from hearing loss at a young age. Suggest what causes this.
3. What is the name of the three bones in the middle ear?
4. The ear drum can be damaged by poking a sharp object in the ear. True or false?

1. 10Hz and 25000Hz. 2. The loud sounds that they are exposed to cause excessive wear of the ear bones (ossicles). 3. The ossicles. 4. True

4.5 Forces and their effects

Learning Summary

After studying this section you should be able to:

- draw arrows on diagrams to show forces
- describe forces as being due to one object acting on another
- understand that weight is a force that acts on a mass
- decide whether forces are balanced or unbalanced
- explain how resistive forces act against motion

What do forces do?

> You should always use a phrase like this when describing a force.

Forces are acting everywhere. No matter where you look, you will see evidence of things **pushing** and **pulling** other things.

Forces can start and stop things from moving, cause changes in direction and change the shape of things when they squash or bend or stretch or twist them.

> **Key Point**
>
> Forces are described by a phrase such as object A pulls or pushes object B.

When you draw forces on a diagram, you should use an arrow to show the direction of the push or pull. Here are some examples:

Figure 4.17

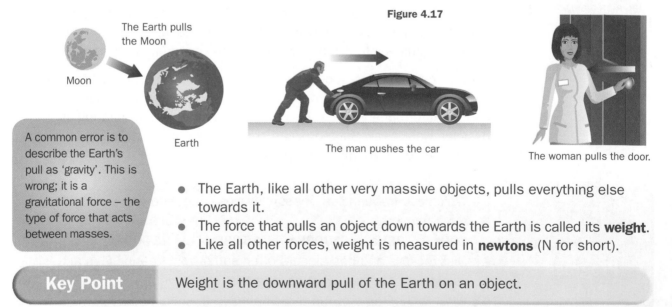

The Earth pulls the Moon

Moon

Earth

The man pushes the car

The woman pulls the door.

> A common error is to describe the Earth's pull as 'gravity'. This is wrong; it is a gravitational force – the type of force that acts between masses.

- The Earth, like all other very massive objects, pulls everything else towards it.
- The force that pulls an object down towards the Earth is called its **weight**.
- Like all other forces, weight is measured in **newtons** (N for short).

> **Key Point**
>
> Weight is the downward pull of the Earth on an object.

On Earth the weight of each kilogram of material is about 10N, so a 25kg sack of potatoes is pulled towards the Earth with a force of 250N.

The Moon also pulls things towards it but with a smaller force; on the Moon the potatoes would weigh about 38N.

Staying still

Look around you – you are surrounded by things that are not moving. Perhaps you are sitting at a desk that is not moving, or you may be sitting in a comfortable chair that is not moving. Even if you are reading this sitting on a moving bus, you can look out of the window and see things that are not moving.

Key Point

Everything that you can see has at least one force acting on it – the Earth's pull.

A common question in KS3 tests is to compare two forces acting on an object that is not moving. They are balanced – equal in size and opposite in direction.

If something is not moving there must also be another force pushing or pulling it so that the forces are **balanced**.

When you sit on a chair it changes shape; the springs and cushion get squashed so that they push up on you. You now have two equal-sized forces acting on you in opposite directions – the forces on you are balanced.

Here are some more examples of balanced forces.

Figure 4.18

The upward push of the shelf

The downward pull of the Earth

The left hand team's pull on the rope

The right hand team's pull on the rope

Floating and sinking

The correct description of this force is 'the water pushes the ball'.

- If you push a plastic ball into a bucket of water, you can feel the water pushing it back up – the more you push it in, the bigger the upward push of the water becomes.
- When a ball floats the forces on it are balanced; the upward push of the water is equal in size to the downward pull of the Earth.
- An object sinks if its weight is greater than the upward push of the water.

Figure 4.19 The water pushes up on the ball

A heavier ball has to displace more water because it needs a bigger upward force to balance its weight.

Air also pushes up on things; it is the upward push of the air that causes a hydrogen-filled balloon to rise.

A hydrogen-filled balloon rises because the upward push of the air is greater than the downward pull of the Earth.

Progress Check

1 If two forces acting on an object are equal in size and opposite in direction, are they balanced or unbalanced?

2 Complete the sentence:

When you sit on a chair, the downward pull of the

_____ is balanced by the _____

push of the _____ .

3 Describe the two forces that act on a ball floating on water. How can you tell that these forces are balanced?

1. Balanced 2. Earth; upward; chair.
3. The Earth pulls the ball down. The water pushes the ball up. The ball is not moving.

Getting moving

Key Point

To start or stop movement, to speed up or slow down, there needs to be an unbalanced force.

Figure 4.20

This unbalanced force makes the cyclist speed up

And this one slows him down

A common error is to describe air resistance as friction. This is wrong. Frictional forces oppose objects from sliding over each other – see page 100.

A train, a car, a bus, a bike and a person walking all need a force to make them move. Can you identify the forces shown in the diagrams of the cyclist (Figure 4.20)? The one on the left is the **driving** force that pushes the cycle along; the one on the right is the **air resistance** that acts against the cyclist's motion. Anyone who has ever ridden a bicycle has felt the effect of air resistance; the faster you go, the bigger this resistive force gets as you have to push more air out of the way each second.

When you are riding a bicycle there are always resistive forces.
● Most of the resistance to motion comes from the air.
● There are also resistive forces in places such as the wheel bearings that oppose a cyclist's motion.

Because of these resistive forces, you have to keep pedalling just to maintain a steady speed. Putting the brakes on creates an extra **resistive** force so that you slow down more rapidly.

The driving force and the resistive force are both at work when a cyclist is pedalling.
● For the cyclist to speed up, the driving force needs to be bigger than the resistive force.
● If the resistive force is bigger than the driving force, the cyclist slows down.
● Cyclists usually stop pedalling when they brake, so there is no driving force, only the resistive force acting.

These are all examples of unbalanced forces.

When you get on a bicycle and start to pedal the resistive force is small at first so you speed up quite rapidly.

- As your speed increases so does the resistive force.
- Eventually you get to a speed where the resistive force is equal in size to the driving force.
- When this happens you stop speeding up and travel at a constant speed.

The forces acting on an object moving in a straight line at a constant speed are balanced. They are the same size but act in opposite directions so that their combined effect is just as if there was no force acting at all.

> The forces on an object are balanced when it is not moving or not changing its speed or direction.

Unbalanced forces are needed to cause any change in motion. A change in direction needs an unbalanced force. The picture shows a girl on a trampoline. To make her move up when she bounces, the upward push of the trampoline has to be bigger than the downward pull of the Earth.

When the girl has lost contact with the trampoline and is moving upwards, the Earth's pull is unbalanced. This causes her to slow down and change direction, making her fall again.

Figure 4.21

Photodisc / Thinkstock

Progress Check

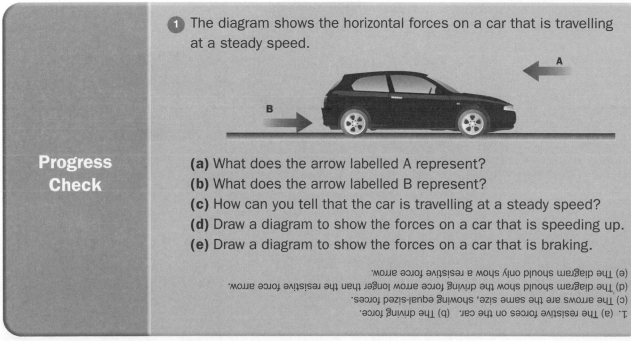

1 The diagram shows the horizontal forces on a car that is travelling at a steady speed.

(a) What does the arrow labelled A represent?

(b) What does the arrow labelled B represent?

(c) How can you tell that the car is travelling at a steady speed?

(d) Draw a diagram to show the forces on a car that is speeding up.

(e) Draw a diagram to show the forces on a car that is braking.

1. (a) The resistive forces on the car. (b) The driving force.
(c) The arrows are the same size, showing equal-sized forces.
(d) The diagram should show the driving force arrow longer than the resistive force arrow.
(e) The diagram should only show a resistive force arrow.

Resistive forces

When you swim you have to work to push against the water. When you run you have to work to push against the air. You can probably run faster than you can swim because the resistive force from the air is less than that from the water.

There are other resistive forces that act on moving objects. Sometimes their effect is to slow down or stop the motion but they also make motion possible. Without resistive forces we cannot walk, and bikes, cars, buses and trains cannot move.

Key Point	Friction is a resistive force that acts against sliding or slipping.

- If you push a book across a desk, **friction** is the force that slows it down and stops it.
- Friction always acts in the opposite direction to any sliding motion.
- Rough surfaces cause bigger friction forces than smooth ones do, so if you want something to slide you should keep the surface smooth and polished or lubricated.

Ice is a good surface to slide on but a very poor surface to walk or ride a bike on.

When we walk we rely on friction to stop our feet from slipping:
- To walk forwards our feet push backwards on the ground.
- The friction force stops them from moving backwards and pushes us forward.
- Without friction, our feet would just slip and we would not get anywhere!

> It may seem strange that we have to push backwards to move forwards. You also do this when you push away from the side of a swimming pool.

Figure 4.22

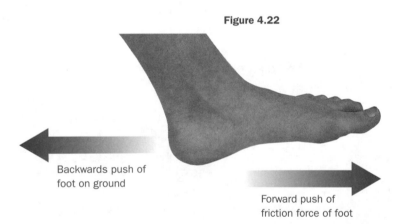

Backwards push of foot on ground

Forward push of friction force of foot

Trains need friction between the wheels and the rails. When wet leaves get on the track the friction force is reduced and the train wheels slip.

> A common error is to state that the skydiver starts to move upwards when the parachute is opened.

Parachutists depend on resistive forces to slow them down. A skydiver who jumps from an aircraft speeds up to a speed of about 60m/s. At this speed the air resistance balances the Earth's pull on the skydiver. Opening the parachute causes the air resistance to get bigger, so the forces acting on the skydiver are no longer balanced. The skydiver now slows down.

Eventually the skydiver falls at a much lower speed with the Earth's pull and the air resistance once again in balance.

Figure 4.23 Forces on a skydiver

Air resistance

Earth's pull

Progress Check

1 When a parachutist opens her parachute, what happens to:

(a) the upward force acting on her?

(b) the downward force acting on her?

(c) her speed?

(d) her direction of travel?

2 When we walk, the force that pushes us forwards is due to friction between our feet and the ground. True or false?

3 'Friction stops things from moving.' Explain whether this is true or false.

3. False. Without friction people would not be able to walk and wheel-based vehicles would not be able to move.   1. (a) It increases. (b) It stays the same. (c) It decreases. (d) It stays the same.   2. True

4.6 Speeding up

Learning Summary

After studying this section you should be able to:

- compare the speeds of moving objects by comparing the times taken to travel a given distance
- calculate the speed of a moving object
- use the relationship between speed, distance and time to calculate journey times and distances
- interpret graphs that represent motion

Who won the race?

Sprinters, marathon runners and Grand Prix racing drivers all compete over a fixed distance. The winner is the person who arrives at the finishing post in the shortest time. Measured over the whole race, the person who takes the shortest time has the greatest **speed**.

To work out the speed of a moving object two measurements are needed:

- the distance travelled by the object
- the time taken to travel that distance

Figure 4.24 The cyclist's average speed can be worked out from measurements of the distance travelled and the time taken

For example, if a bus travels 60 miles in 2 hours, its average speed is 30mph (miles per hour). This speed is only an average as there would be times when the bus was travelling faster than this and times when it was travelling slower. There would even be times when it was not moving at all.

Speed and velocity are often confused. Velocity is speed but in a certain direction.

Key Point

Average speeds are worked out using the equation:

$$\text{average speed} = \frac{\text{distance travelled}}{\text{time taken}}$$

$$v = \frac{s}{t}$$

The symbol s is used for distance as d is used in other equations for diameter. The symbol v is used for speed and velocity.

Although we use miles and hours when talking about everyday journeys, the units used in science are metres (m) and seconds (s).

Example

Calculate the average speed of a motorcycle that takes 6 seconds to travel 90 m.

$$v = \frac{s}{t} = \frac{90m}{6s} = 15m/s$$

Progress Check

1 Complete the sentence:

To work out an average speed, measurements are needed of the distance travelled and the _____ .

2 Here are the times taken for three runners to complete a 100m race.

(a) Who won the race?

Runner	Time (s)
Mel	14.5
Sarfraz	15.4
Sam	12.5

(b) Calculate Sam's average speed.

1. time taken 2. (a) Sam (b) 8.0 m/s

How long does it take?

If you are walking to catch a bus or travelling to an airport or ferry port, you need to know what time to set off so that you arrive in time. To estimate the time for a journey, two pieces of information are needed:

- the distance to travel
- the average speed

You may find the 'triangle method' useful here. Cover the one you are trying to find with your thumb and it will show the expression.

In good weather conditions, provided there are no delays such as traffic jams, the average speed of a car travelling on a motorway is about 60 mph. How long would a journey of 150 miles take?

To answer this you need to be able to use the speed equation in the form 'time = ...'.

Key Point

The speed equation can be written in three different ways. In symbols, these are:

$$v = \frac{s}{t} \qquad t = \frac{s}{v} \qquad s = v \times t$$

The Key Point box on page 102 shows three different ways of writing the same equation. You can now work out the journey time using $t = \frac{s}{v}$.

You should get $2\frac{1}{2}$ hours.

The Key Point box on page 102

Progress Check

1 Work out the quantities that go in the blank spaces in the table. Take care to write the correct unit with your answer.

	Distance travelled	Time taken	Average speed
(a)	300m	6s	
(b)	6cm	1.5s	
(c)		5 hours	125mph
(d)	1750 miles		500mph
(e)	7.5m	0.5s	
(f)	1500m		25m/s
(g)		4.5s	8m/s

1. (a) 50m/s (b) 4cm/s (c) 625 miles (d) 3.5 hours (e) 15m/s (f) 60s (g) 36m

Using graphs

If you walk to the end of the street and then back again, the distance that you have travelled is always increasing.

Two types of line graph that are often used to show an object's motion are:
- **distance–time graphs** – the distance travelled by an object can only increase with time
- **speed–time graphs** – speed can increase and decrease so the line can go down as well as up

Here are two graphs that show the same journey.

Figure 4.25

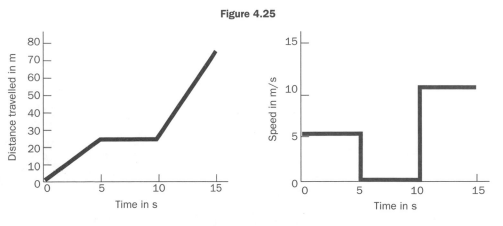

When answering questions about graphs that represent motion, always double check whether the graph is a distance–time graph or a speed–time graph.

If the graph line is horizontal then the object is not moving.

Both graphs show a constant speed of 5m/s for the first 5s, followed by a 5s rest and then a constant speed of 10m/s for the next 5s. Notice how, on the distance–time graph, the steeper the line the greater the speed.

Key Point

The slope, or gradient, of a distance–time graph represents speed.

The greater the slope, the faster the object is moving.

Progress Check

1 Use words from the list to fill in the blanks.

decrease   distance   increase   speed

Motion can be represented by a _____ –time or a speed–time graph. The distance an object travels cannot _____ , but its speed can _____ or decrease. The slope of a distance–time graph represents _____ .

1. distance; decrease; increase; speed

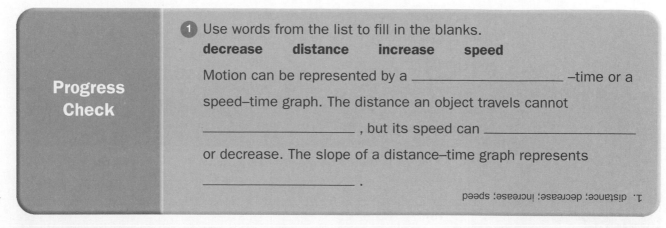

4.7 Pressure and moments

Learning Summary

After studying this section you should be able to:

- explain how the pressure caused by a force depends on the area that it acts on
- use the relationship between pressure, force and area
- describe the turning effect of a force and calculate its value
- apply the principle of moments

Under pressure

Pushing a drawing pin into a board, cutting food with a knife and ice-skating are just three everyday examples of using a force to create a large pressure.

Pressure describes the effect a force has in cutting or piercing the surface it acts on:

- Knives, scissors, needles and drawing pins are all designed to cut or pierce. They create a large pressure by applying a force onto a small area.

Figure 4.26

- Skis and caterpillar tracks on heavy vehicles are examples of spreading a force over a large area to reduce the pressure it causes.

Figure 4.27

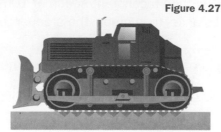

A common error in tests is to state that 'the pressure acts over a large area'. Do not confuse the terms 'force' and 'pressure'.

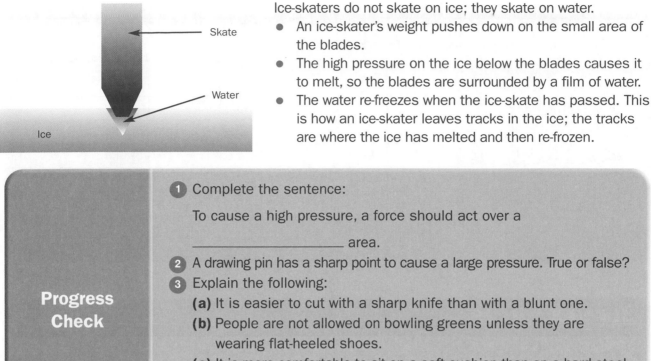

Ice-skaters do not skate on ice; they skate on water.
- An ice-skater's weight pushes down on the small area of the blades.
- The high pressure on the ice below the blades causes it to melt, so the blades are surrounded by a film of water.
- The water re-freezes when the ice-skate has passed. This is how an ice-skater leaves tracks in the ice; the tracks are where the ice has melted and then re-frozen.

Progress Check

1 Complete the sentence:

To cause a high pressure, a force should act over a

_____ area.

2 A drawing pin has a sharp point to cause a large pressure. True or false?

3 Explain the following:

(a) It is easier to cut with a sharp knife than with a blunt one.

(b) People are not allowed on bowling greens unless they are wearing flat-heeled shoes.

(c) It is more comfortable to sit on a soft cushion than on a hard stool.

1. small 2. True 3. (a) The sharp knife has a smaller surface area so it exerts a bigger pressure. (b) High-heeled shoes have a small surface area. The pressure they exert creates dents in the surface of the bowling green. (c) The cushion changes shape so there is more surface area in contact with the body, causing less pressure.

Quantifying pressure

Pressure is calculated as the force acting on each cm^2 or m^2 of surface area using the formula:

$$pressure = \frac{force}{area} \text{ or } P = \frac{F}{A}$$

It is measured in N/m^2 or pascals (Pa). When the area involved is small, the unit N/cm^2 is used.

> Always give the correct unit, Pa or N/m^2

Example

A bulldozer weighs 150 000N. To stop it from sinking into the soft mud it moves on caterpillar tracks. The area of the tracks in contact with the ground is $10m^2$. Calculate the pressure on the ground.

$$Pressure = \frac{force}{area}$$

$$= \frac{150\,000N}{10m^2}$$

$$= 15\,000Pa$$

> You may use this triangle $\frac{F}{P\ A}$

> You need to be able to use all three forms of the equation to answer questions aimed at the highest levels.

Like the speed equation, the pressure equation can be written in three different ways:

$$P = \frac{F}{A} \qquad A = \frac{F}{P} \qquad F = P \times A$$

Progress Check

① Pressure is calculated as the force acting on each cm² or m² of surface area using the formula:

	Force	Area	Pressure
(a)	25N	2m²	
(b)		0.5m²	500Pa
(c)	50N		500Pa
(d)	100N	0.1cm²	
(e)		3m²	100 000Pa

1. (a) 12.5N/m² (b) 250N (c) 0.1m² (d) 1000N/cm² (e) 300 000N

Turning forces

Whenever we turn on a tap, push the pedals on a bike or open a door we are using a force to turn something round.

Key Point

The point that things turn around is called the pivot.

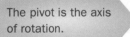
The pivot is the axis of rotation.

In the case of a tap, the pivot is at the centre of the tap. A door pivots around the hinge. The diagram shows the force and the pivot when a pedal is turned.

Figure 4.28

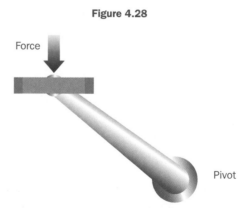

Force

Pivot

If you try closing a door by pushing it at different places, you realise why door handles are placed as far from the pivot as possible.

The effect that a force has in turning something round is called the **moment** of the force. It depends on:
- the size of the force
- how far away from the pivot it is applied

Key Point

The further away from the pivot it is applied, the bigger the turning effect of a force.

Key Point

The moment of a force is calculated using the relationship:
moment = force × perpendicular distance to pivot.

The perpendicular distance is the shortest distance from the force line to the pivot.

Figure 4.29

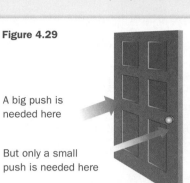

A big push is needed here

But only a small push is needed here

The door handle is placed as far from the pivot as possible to increase the turning effect of the force.

Progress Check

1. Each of the diagrams below shows something that can be made to turn round. On each diagram, mark the pivot and a force that would cause turning.

2. Calculate the moment of the force being used to tighten the wheelnut.

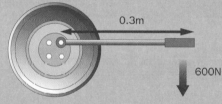

0.3m

600N

1. Door handle: the pivot is at the centre of the handle and the force should push up or down on the handle.   Wheelbarrow: the pivot is at the base of the wheel and the force should push up on the handle.   Spanner: the pivot is at the centre of the nut and the force should be to the left or the right.   2. 180Nm

A question of balance

A seesaw has two forces acting on it:

Figure 4.30

An anticlockwise movement

A clockwise movement

> Questions in tests will normally involve just one force on each side of the pivot.

- Each force has a turning effect but they are acting in opposition.
- If the moments of the forces are unequal, then the one with the bigger moment wins.
- If the forces have equal moments the seesaw is balanced.

This is an example of the **principle of moments**.

Key Point

The principle of moments states that:
If an object is balanced, the sum of the clockwise moments about a pivot is equal to the sum of the anticlockwise moments about the same pivot.

Progress Check

1 The diagrams show some seesaws. For diagrams A, B, C and D, decide whether each one is balanced, or whether it will rotate clockwise or anticlockwise. For diagrams E and F work out the size of the force needed to balance the seesaw.

20N 10N 5m 2m A
15N 20N 6m 4m B
30N 10N 15N 4m 3m 3m C
8N 10N 4m 3m D
15N 2m 6m E
6m 30N 2m F

1. A: rotate anticlockwise; B: rotate anticlockwise; C: balanced; D: rotate anticlockwise; E: 5N; F: 10N

4.8 Electricity

Learning Summary

After studying this section you should be able to:

- recall the symbols used in a circuit diagram
- state that the current is the same at all points in a series circuit
- understand how current divides along the branches of a parallel circuit
- explain how voltage is measured
- compare the advantages of series and parallel circuits

Current in circuits

> For a current to pass, the positive and negative terminals have to be joined by a conductor.

Using a lamp and a dry cell or a low voltage power pack, you can easily see that electricity is not like water or gas that flow along a pipe and come out when a tap is opened.

You need to have a complete route from the cell to the lamp and back again. This route is called a circuit.

| **Key Point** | In a circuit there is a complete current path from the positive terminal of the battery or power supply to the negative terminal. |

Remember, a conductor allows electricity to pass through it but an insulator does not.

If there is a break in the circuit, the lamp goes out. You can use a circuit with a break in it to test which materials are **conductors** and which are **insulators**.

Air is normally an insulator, so an air gap in a circuit can be used as a switch.
- If the gap is closed using a conducting material, the circuit is switched on.
- The circuit is switched off when the gap is open.

A circuit diagram is a shorthand way of showing how to connect the components in a circuit.

Figure 4.31 uses circuit symbols to show a lamp that can be switched on and off.

Figure 4.31

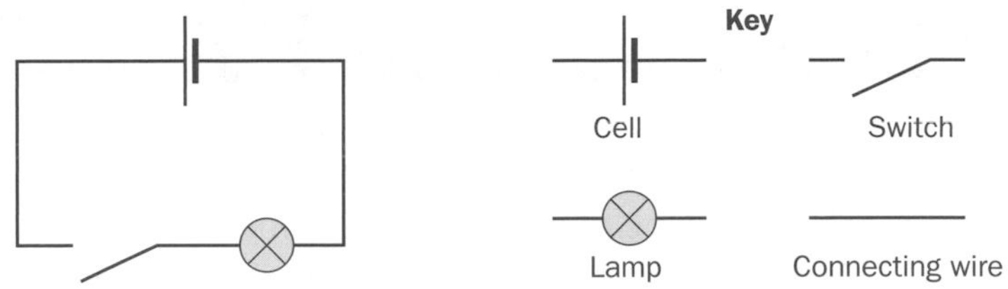

Key

Cell   Switch

Lamp   Connecting wire

Here are some more symbols that you may find useful.

Figure 4.32

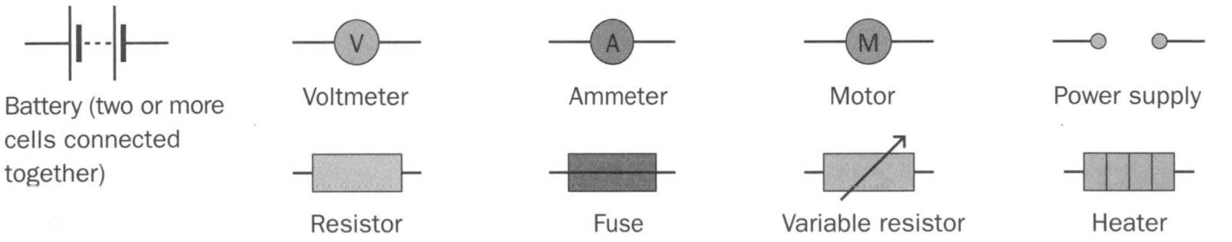

Battery (two or more cells connected together)   Voltmeter   Ammeter   Motor   Power supply

Resistor   Fuse   Variable resistor   Heater

Progress Check

1. Complete the sentence:

   Electricity is used to _____ things up, make things _____ and make things give out _____ .
2. An insulator allows electricity to pass through it easily. True or false?
3. In a circuit there is a complete conducting path from the positive to the negative terminal of the battery or power supply. True or false?

1. heat; move; light 2. False 3. True

Different types of circuit

There are two different ways of connecting two lamps to one cell or power supply:

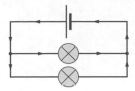

Figure 4.33 A series circuit and a parallel circuit.

- The circuit on the left is called a **series** circuit. In a series circuit the current from the cell passes through each lamp in turn, one after the other.
- A **parallel** circuit is shown on the right. In a parallel circuit the current splits at the junction before the lamps and rejoins at the junction after the lamps.

Electronic systems, such as those in computers, radios and televisions, contain many series circuits but most household mains appliances are in a parallel circuit. The exception is some types of Christmas tree lights.

> The components in a series circuit are either all turned on or all turned off.

In a series circuit, a break anywhere in a circuit turns the whole circuit off. With a parallel circuit, switches can be put in the branches of the circuit so that each switch controls just one device.

Controlling the current

> Make sure that you know the circuit symbols for common components, such as lamps and variable resistors.

The brightness of a lamp shows the size of the electric current passing in a circuit; the brighter the lamp, the greater the current passing. The current can be made bigger or smaller if a variable resistor is included in the circuit.

Figure 4.34 shows a common type of variable resistor and the circuit diagram shows how it is connected in a lamp-dimming circuit.

Figure 4.34 A variable resistor connected in a lamp-dimming circuit

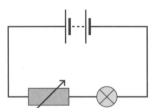 

Moving the slider to one end of the variable resistor makes the lamp light at its brightest. The lamp is dimmest when the slider is moved to the opposite end.

Variable resistors can control other things besides lamps. They act as the volume control on radios and they can also be used to control the speed of an electric motor.

Progress Check

1. **(a)** Which type of circuit would you use for lighting your bedroom and your sister's bedroom, series or parallel?
   (b) Explain why this circuit should be used.
2. If you increase the resistance of a variable resistor, what happens to the current passing in it?
3. Complete the sentence:

   Decreasing the resistance in a circuit causes the current to

   _____ .

1. (a) Parallel (b) So that each lamp can be switched on and off independently of the other lamp.
2. It decreases. 3. increase

Measuring voltage

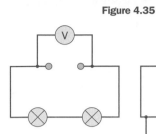

Figure 4.35

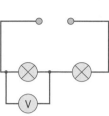

This voltmeter measures the voltage of the power supply.

This voltmeter measures the voltage across the lamp.

Batteries can have different voltages and laboratory power supplies usually have different voltage settings.

The diagrams show how a voltmeter is used to measure the voltage of a power supply and across one of the lamps in a series circuit.

Key Point

A voltmeter is a device that measures voltage in volts (V). It is always connected in parallel with a power supply or component.

If you connect a voltmeter in series in a circuit, the circuit will not work because a voltmeter has a very high resistance.

Voltage is a measure of the energy transfer to and from the charged particles that carry the current in a circuit. Increasing the voltage in the circuit shown above increases the brightness of the lamps. This is because:

- increasing the voltage increases the current
- the moving charged particles have more energy to transfer from the power supply to the lamps.

Progress Check

1. To measure the voltage across a lamp, should a voltmeter be connected in series or in parallel with it?
2. What two factors determine how bright a lamp appears in a circuit?

1. In parallel. 2. The current and the voltage.

Measuring current

A lamp 'blows' when part of the filament becomes so hot that it melts, breaking the circuit.

Sometimes the current passing in a circuit may be so small that it is not enough to light a lamp. Or it may be too large and would cause the lamp to 'blow'.

An **ammeter**:

- detects a greater range of current than a lamp does
- gives more precise measurements and enables you to make comparisons.

Key Point

An ammeter is a device that measures the size of an electric current in amps (A). Ammeters are always connected in series in a circuit.

Ammeters are either digital, which are easy to read, or analogue, which involve a needle moving over a scale. Analogue meters call for more care when taking readings, as you have to interpret the scale divisions and make judgements about readings between scale divisions.

The diagrams below show how to connect an ammeter to measure the current passing into and out of a lamp.

The direction of a current is always taken as being from positive to negative. This means that current passes into the lamp from the positive battery terminal and out of the lamp towards the negative terminal.

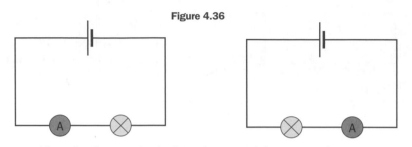

Figure 4.36

Measuring the current going into a lamp... and the current going out.

Most people are surprised when they do this experiment and find that **the current coming out of the lamp is the same as that going in**. The lamp does not use up any current at all. The results obtained from the next circuit confirm this.

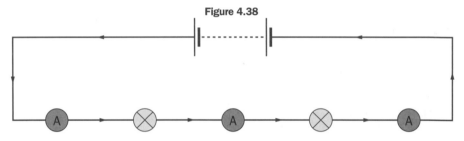

Figure 4.38

All the ammeter readings are the same; the lamps have not used any current.

Key Point   The current is the same at all points in a series circuit

This may seem strange because without a current the lamps do not work. So how do lamps produce light?
- What comes out of a lamp is **energy**, in the form of heat and light.
- The current in a circuit transfers energy from the source, the battery or power supply, to the lamp and other components, such as motors or heaters.

Figure 4.37 Charge flow in a circuit containing a cell and a lamp

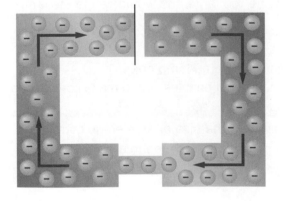

Energy is transferred around a circuit by moving charged particles. In metals the moving particles are electrons; these carry a negative charge. Electrons cannot move in an insulator but they are free to move around in a conductor. The electron movement is from negative to positive, even though we always mark current directions as being from positive to negative.

The diagram shows a model of charge flow in a circuit containing a cell and a lamp. The narrow part of the circuit represents the lamp filament.

Changing the current

In the section 'controlling current' you learned how a variable resistor can be used to vary the current in a circuit. The size of the current that passes in a circuit depends on:

- the **voltage** of the current source
- the **resistance** of the circuit

> Resistance describes the opposition to electric current.

A variable resistor works by changing the resistance. The more resistance there is, the smaller the current that passes.

When you increase the voltage that drives the current in a circuit, a bigger force acts on the moving charges. The charge travels round the circuit at a greater rate, so increasing the current.

Figure 4.38 shows that when you add more lamps in a series circuit, the current becomes less because you are increasing the circuit resistance.

Figure 4.38

One lamp

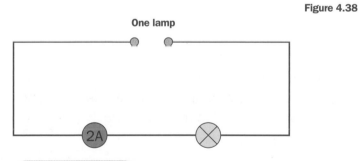

Two lamps in series

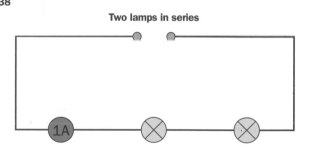

> When lamps are added in parallel the circuit has less resistance as more current can pass.

Adding more lamps in parallel causes more current in the circuit because there are more routes available for the current to pass through, as Figure 4.39 shows.

This circuit shows that when the current splits at a junction, the sum of the currents along the branches is equal to the current from the power supply.

Figure 4.39 Two lamps in parallel

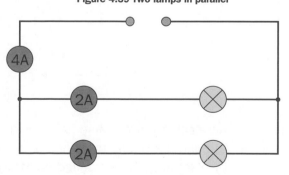

Key Point	In a parallel circuit, the current that passes into a junction is equal to the current that passes out.

Progress Check	1 What happens to the current in a circuit when more lamps are added in series with the power supply? 2 What happens to the current in a circuit when more lamps are added in parallel with the power supply?

1. It decreases. 2. It increases.

Some effects of an electric current

When an electric current passes through a wire it produces a magnetic field around it.

Figure 4.40 shows lines of force around a wire.

Figure 4.40

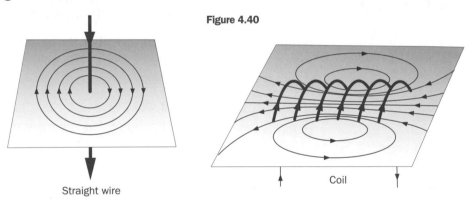

Straight wire   Coil

Figure 4.41 shows a coil of wire connected to a power supply. As electricity passes through the wire, energy is transferred to the water and the temperature rises. An electric current has a heating effect.

Figure 4.41

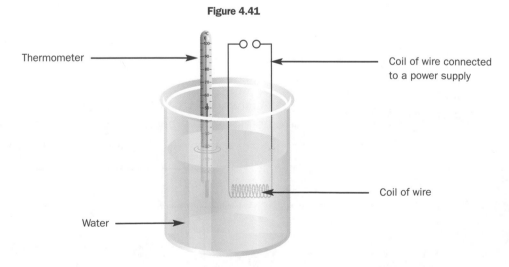

Thermometer

Coil of wire connected to a power supply

Coil of wire

Water

An electric current also has a chemical effect. When electricity passes through a molten substance or a solution, the substance may be split up by electricity. This is called **electrolysis**.

Assessment questions

Levels 3–4

1. **(a)** Name two non-renewable energy sources.

_____

_____ **[2]**

(b) Name two renewable energy sources.

_____

_____ **[2]**

(c) The diagram shows a circuit that uses two switches to control a lamp.

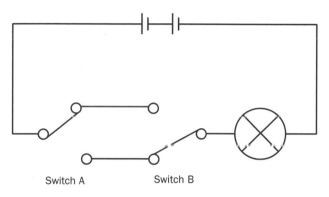

Switch A   Switch B

(i) Complete the table to show when the lamp is 'on' and 'off'.

Switch A	Switch B	Lamp
Up	Down	Off
Up	Up	
Down	Up	
Down	Down	

[3]

(ii) The switches are placed at the positions shown in the diagram. Write down two ways of switching the lamp on.

_____

_____ **[2]**

(iii) Suggest a use for this circuit.

_____ **[1]**

Assessment questions

2. This question is about reflection of light.

(a) Which diagram shows the reflection of light at a mirror correctly?

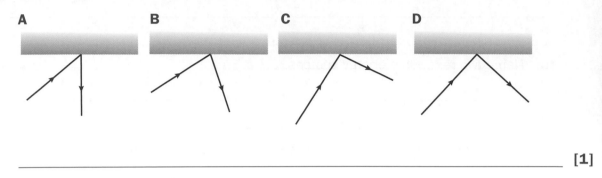

_____ **[1]**

(b) How is reflection of light from this book different from reflection of light from a mirror?

_____

_____ **[1]**

(c) A candle is placed in front of a mirror.

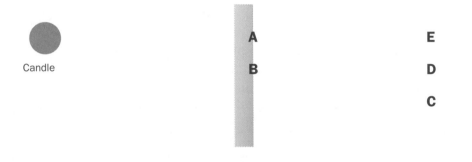

(i) Which letter shows the position of the image of the candle?

_____ **[1]**

(ii) Write down **two** ways in which the candle and its image are similar.

(1) _____ **[1]**

(2) _____ **[1]**

Assessment questions

Levels 5–6

3. A car is travelling along a road at 30m/s. The car driver sees some traffic lights at red and brakes to a halt. The graph shows how the speed of the car changes from the moment that the driver sees the traffic lights.

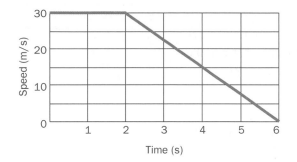

(a) How far did the car travel before the brakes were applied? Use distance = speed × time.

_____

_____ **[2]**

(b) After the brakes were applied, how long did it take for the car to stop?

_____ **[1]**

(c) The average speed while the car was braking was 15m/s. Calculate the distance the car travelled after the brakes were applied.

_____

_____ **[2]**

(d) What was the total stopping distance of the car?

_____ **[1]**

4. An ice skater has a weight of 600N. She exerts a pressure of 1 200 000Pa on the ice when skating on both skates.

(a) Calculate the total area of the blades of her ice skates.

Use the formula pressure = $\dfrac{\text{force}}{\text{area}}$

_____

_____ **[3]**

(b) What happens to the pressure when she lifts one skate off the ice?

_____

_____ **[1]**

Assessment questions

5. An ammeter and a voltmeter are used to measure the current that passes in a filament lamp and the voltage across it.

	Ammeter connected	Voltmeter connected
A	in series	in series
B	in parallel	in parallel
C	in parallel	in series
D	in series	in parallel

(a) Which line in the table shows how the ammeter and voltmeter should be connected to the lamp?

_____ **[1]**

(b) The graph shows how the current in the lamp depends on the voltage across it.

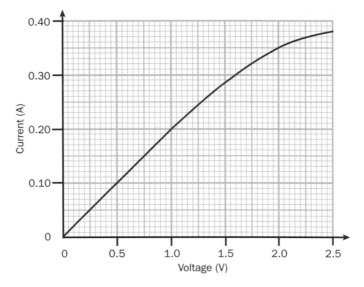

(i) Use the graph to explain whether doubling the voltage always causes the current to double.

_____

_____

_____

_____ **[3]**

(ii) Give two reasons why the lamp becomes brighter when the voltage across it is doubled.

(1) _____

_____ **[2]**

(2) _____

_____ **[2]**

5 The Environment, Earth and Universe

			Studied	Revised	Assessment questions
5.1	Geological activity	– What are rocks made from? – Weathering – Types of rock – The rock cycle			
5.2	The Earth and beyond	– The view from Earth – The view from outside			
5.3	How the environment changes	– Introduction – Acid rain – Monitoring air and water pollution – Global warming – Depletion of the ozone layer – Volcanoes and earthquakes			

5.1 Geological activity

After studying this section you should be able to:

Learning Summary

- describe rock specimens in terms of texture and relate this to properties such as porosity
- describe physical weathering and chemical processes by which rocks are weathered
- describe how fragments of rock are transported and deposited as layers of sediment
- describe how sediments become sedimentary rocks
- describe how metamorphic rocks are formed
- describe how igneous rocks can be formed by crystallising magma
- explain how different crystals of different sizes are formed
- explain how the rock cycle links the three types of rock

What are rocks made from?

Rocks are made from a wide range of chemical compounds called **minerals**.

When you look at a rock carefully you might see different bits that fit together. Sometimes these bits are small **crystals** and sometimes they are small **grains**.

If they are very closely packed together then water does not pass through the rock. If there are gaps between these, water can pass through. These rocks are said to be **permeable**.

Weathering

The terms 'weathering' and 'erosion' are often confused. Erosion involves the breaking down of rocks by movement of rivers, ice, sea and wind.

Many buildings are made of rocks. Over a period of years these rocks are broken down by weathering. The photograph below shows the weathering of rocks.

Weathering can take place in three main ways:

1 Mechanical weathering
During the day rocks heat up and expand. At night they cool and this cooling causes stresses within the rock. When this happens over and over again it breaks down the rock. If there are cracks in the rock, water gets into the cracks. When water freezes, ice forms and expands. This breaks down the rocks. This is sometimes called 'freeze-thaw'.

Figure 5.01 Weathering of rocks

Figure 5.02 Repeated freezing and thawing breaks down rocks

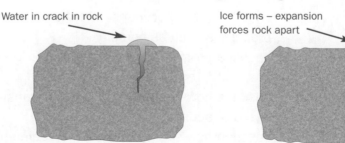

Water in crack in rock

Ice forms – expansion forces rock apart

2 Chemical weathering
This is the breaking down of rocks by chemical reaction.

Limestone is broken down by rain water. Rain water contains dissolved carbon dioxide. This forms carbonic acid.

water + carbon dioxide ⟶ carbonic acid

You may see this word equation written as a symbol equation.
$H_2O + CO_2 \longrightarrow H_2CO_3$

You may see this word equation written as a symbol equation.

$$CaCO_3 + H_2CO_3 \longrightarrow Ca(HCO_3)_2$$

Carbonic acid attacks the limestone forming calcium hydrogencarbonate, which is soluble in water.

calcium carbonate + carbonic acid $\longrightarrow$ calcium hydrogencarbonate

This weathering is speeded up when other acids are present in the atmosphere from acid rain.

3 **Biological weathering**
As plant roots grow they cause stresses on rocks and can cause them to break up.

Figure 5.03 Biological weathering

The rock fragments produced by these forms of weathering often get washed into rivers. As the fragments get carried along, they become more rounded, losing sharp edges. As the speed of the river slows, the fragments are deposited on the riverbed. Heavy fragments drop first and fine fragments are carried further.

Figure 5.04 Conglomerate

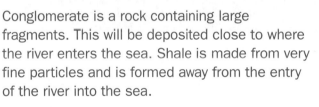

Conglomerate is a rock containing large fragments. This will be deposited close to where the river enters the sea. Shale is made from very fine particles and is formed away from the entry of the river into the sea.

Figure 5.05 Formation of conglomerate and shale

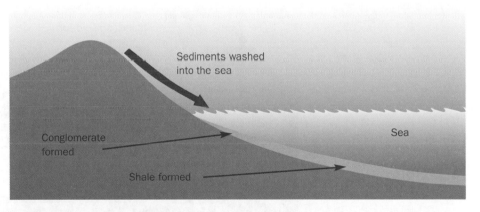

Types of rock

There are three different types of rock in the Earth.

Sedimentary rocks

These rocks are formed when bits of existing rocks, broken off by weathering and erosion, settle as sediment. This is then compressed by other rocks and cemented together.

The rocks are not crystalline but are made up of grains. Sedimentary rocks may contain **fossils**. Chalk and limestone are sedimentary rocks.

Much of Great Britain is a limestone area. Great Britain was once near the equator and covered with a tropical ocean. The limestone is the remains of the shells of sea creatures.

Metamorphic rocks

Metamorphic rocks are formed when high temperatures and high pressures act on sedimentary rocks. These rocks may be non-crystalline or may contain tiny crystals.

Metamorphic rocks may contain distorted crystals. Marble is a metamorphic rock made from limestone. Slate is a metamorphic rock made from the action of high temperatures and high pressures on mud.

Igneous rocks

Igneous rocks are formed when the hot magma inside the Earth is cooled and crystallises. The size of the crystals depends on the rate of cooling. If the cooling is rapid, small crystals are formed. Slow cooling produces larger crystals.

Granite and basalt are two igneous rocks. Granite has larger crystals as it crystallises slowly inside the Earth. Basalt has small crystals as the crystallisation takes place rapidly on the Earth's surface.

> Metamorphic rocks are usually much harder than sedimentary rocks.

> Igneous rocks cannot contain fossils.

> Looking at a sample you will see crystals of different minerals – quartz is white, mica is shiny black and feldspar is brown.

The rock cycle

Inside the Earth, existing rocks can be taken back into the magma and new rocks formed. This is summarised in the diagram.

Figure 5.06 The rock cycle

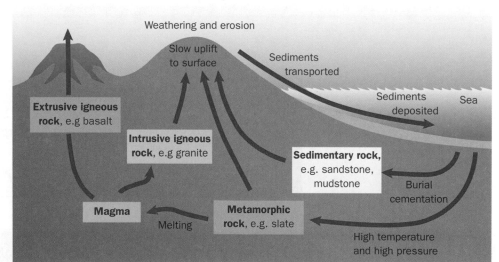

Rocks are being broken down and new rocks are being formed all the time. When the magma crystallises, igneous rocks are produced. These rocks are broken down by weathering and erosion to form sediments. Sediments are deposited and converted into sedimentary rocks. Sedimentary rocks can be converted into metamorphic rocks by high temperatures and high pressures. Rocks returning to the magma complete the cycle.

The rock cycle is driven by two energy processes. On the surface, processes are powered by the Sun's energy. Within the Earth, energy is provided by radioactive decay.

Progress Check

1. What are the three types of weathering?
2. How does 'freeze-thaw' break up rocks?
3. The composition of conglomerate can be very varied. Suggest why.
4. Which processes are used when
   (a) sedimentary rocks are converted into metamorphic rocks?
   (b) magma is converted into igneous rocks?
   (c) sediments are converted into sedimentary rocks?
   (d) igneous rocks are broken into sediments?

1. Mechanical, chemical and biological.
2. Water in cracks freezes and expands, forces rock apart, thaws, process repeats.
3. Depends on which rocks are broken down.
4. (a) High temperature and high pressure. (b) Cooling and crystallising. (c) Transported, settles, compressed (or compacted), cemented. (d) Weathering and erosion.

5.2 The Earth and beyond

Learning Summary

After studying this section you should be able to:

- understand how the apparent daily movement of the Sun and other stars is caused by the Earth spinning on its axis
- describe the positions of the planets in the Solar System
- explain how planetary orbits are due to gravitational attractive forces
- describe the differences between how the Sun and planets are seen
- state some uses of artificial satellites

The view from Earth

Key Point

Astronomy is the scientific study of celestial bodies, including the planets, stars, galaxies and the complete Universe.

If you are sitting at home reading this, you do not have a sensation of movement. It is not obvious that our **planet** Earth is moving through space with a speed of thousands of metres per second. So it is not surprising that early astronomers made the mistake of thinking that the **Sun** moves around the **Earth**.

On a sunny day you can plot the Sun's path across the sky by watching the movement of a shadow.
- The shadow is longest in the morning and evening when the Sun is low in the sky.
- As the shadow moves round in the morning it gets shorter. It is at its shortest at noon when the Sun has reached its highest point in the sky.
- After noon, the shadow starts to lengthen again. You can see very long shadows near sunset on a sunny evening.

A common error is to confuse the Earth's rotation on its axis with its movement around the Sun.

These changes in a shadow seem to be caused by the Sun moving across the sky – rising in the East and setting in the West. The diagram shows how the Sun appears to move each day.

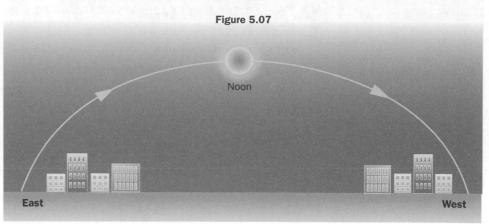

Figure 5.07

Noon

East   West

Figure 5.08

We now know that this 'movement' of the Sun is actually due to the Earth turning round once each day.

The Earth **spins** on its **axis**, an imaginary line going through the centre of the Earth from pole to pole.

Key Point   The Earth makes one complete rotation on its axis in one day.

If you were out in **space**, looking down at the Earth's North Pole, you would see the Earth turning round in an anticlockwise direction.

Key Point   This daily rotation of the Earth causes day and night. It also causes the Sun's apparent movement across the sky.

The diagram shows Britain (highlighted in red) at sunrise, noon and sunset. This is the view you would have if you were looking down at the North Pole. The outer circle of the Earth is the equator.

Figure 5.09

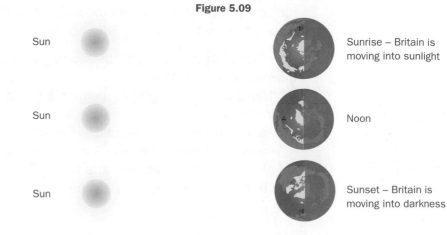

Sun

Sunrise – Britain is moving into sunlight

Sun

Noon

Sun

Sunset – Britain is moving into darkness

Progress Check

1. Use the diagram to state where you would have to look to see the Sun at different times of day.
2. The Sun makes one revolution of the Earth each day. True or false?
3. Complete the sentence:

   The Earth takes _____ to spin once on its axis.

1. To the East at sunrise, overhead at noon and to the West at sunset.
2. False   3. One day or 24 hours.

The amount of daylight varies in **summer** and **winter**, and the highest position of the Sun in the sky also changes with the season.

- Twice a year, at the spring and autumn equinox, day and night are of equal length.
- Summer brings longer days than nights, with the Sun being higher in the sky.
- The diagram shows the Sun's apparent path at three different times of year.

Figure 5.10

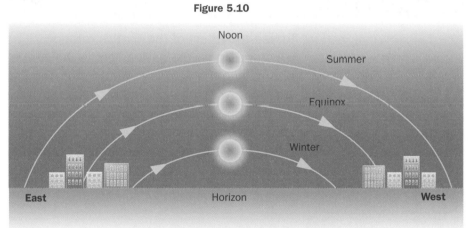

> Questions about the differences in the Sun's daily motion in winter and summer are common in tests.

The number of hours of **daylight** and **darkness** varies throughout the year. This is due to the Earth being **tilted**. The Earth's axis always points in the same direction, towards the star Polaris.

> The Pole itself is light for 24 hours a day in the height of summer.

When it is summer in Britain the **northern hemisphere** is tilted towards the Sun, so we spend more than 12 hours in daylight. The nearer you are to the North Pole in summer, the longer your days are.

Figure 5.11 Summer in the northern hemisphere

Energy from the Sun

This not only makes the days longer, it also means that energy from the Sun is spread over a smaller area than in winter, giving us a warmer climate in summer.

When it is winter in Britain, energy from the Sun is spread over a larger area.

Our Sun is the only **star** that we see during the day; the other stars are there but the bright light from the Sun prevents us from seeing them. Polaris, or the Pole Star, is a very bright star. As mentioned earlier, the Earth's axis points towards the Pole Star, so you can see it by looking in the sky directly north. The diagram shows the Pole Star as it can appear in the winter sky.

Figure 5.12

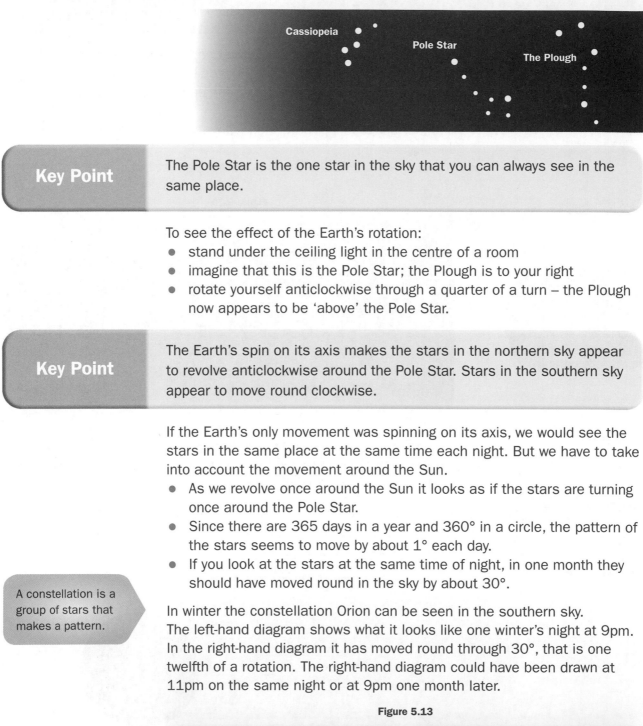

Key Point

The Pole Star is the one star in the sky that you can always see in the same place.

To see the effect of the Earth's rotation:
- stand under the ceiling light in the centre of a room
- imagine that this is the Pole Star; the Plough is to your right
- rotate yourself anticlockwise through a quarter of a turn – the Plough now appears to be 'above' the Pole Star.

Key Point

The Earth's spin on its axis makes the stars in the northern sky appear to revolve anticlockwise around the Pole Star. Stars in the southern sky appear to move round clockwise.

If the Earth's only movement was spinning on its axis, we would see the stars in the same place at the same time each night. But we have to take into account the movement around the Sun.
- As we revolve once around the Sun it looks as if the stars are turning once around the Pole Star.
- Since there are 365 days in a year and 360° in a circle, the pattern of the stars seems to move by about 1° each day.
- If you look at the stars at the same time of night, in one month they should have moved round in the sky by about 30°.

A constellation is a group of stars that makes a pattern.

In winter the constellation Orion can be seen in the southern sky. The left-hand diagram shows what it looks like one winter's night at 9pm. In the right-hand diagram it has moved round through 30°, that is one twelfth of a rotation. The right-hand diagram could have been drawn at 11pm on the same night or at 9pm one month later.

Figure 5.13

Orion at 9pm

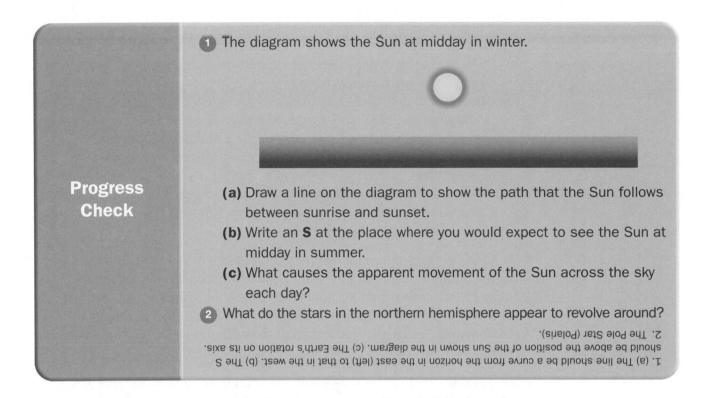

Progress Check

1 The diagram shows the Sun at midday in winter.

(a) Draw a line on the diagram to show the path that the Sun follows between sunrise and sunset.

(b) Write an **S** at the place where you would expect to see the Sun at midday in summer.

(c) What causes the apparent movement of the Sun across the sky each day?

2 What do the stars in the northern hemisphere appear to revolve around?

1. (a) The line should be a curve from the horizon in the east (left) to that in the west. (b) The S should be above the position of the Sun shown in the diagram. (c) The Earth's rotation on its axis. 2. The Pole Star (Polaris).

The view from outside

If you could look at the **Solar System** from a viewpoint where you could see all the planets, what would you see? The most striking object would be the Sun, shining with a brilliant white light. You would also be struck by the colours of the planets and the contrast between the rich orange colour of Venus and the blue planet Earth. Of course, you would only be able to see half of each planet, because planets are only visible by the sunlight that they **reflect** and only the half of each planet facing the Sun would be lit up.

You would notice four planets close to the Sun (see Figure 5.14, p.128):

- Nearest to the Sun is the tiny planet **Mercury**, its surface covered in impact craters.
- Next comes **Venus**, its dense atmosphere reflecting only orange light.
- The third planet out from the Sun is the planet **Earth**.
- The fourth planet out from the Sun, **Mars**, appears a blood-red colour.

From outer space you would not be able to see any evidence of human activity on Earth. You would, however, notice that the Earth has a **satellite** of its own – a moon very similar in size and appearance to Mercury. The Earth's moon takes about 28 days to complete an orbit of the Earth. It takes the same time to spin once on its axis, so the same side of the Moon always faces towards the Earth. Looking at the planets, you would see that:

- they all go round the Sun in the same direction
- the speed of a planet depends on its distance from the Sun
- Mercury moves fastest of all and it also has the shortest distance to travel to complete an orbit.

Moving your eyes further out, you would notice a lot of rocky fragments orbiting the Sun between Mars and the first of the outer planets, Jupiter. These fragments of rock, up to 100km in diameter, form the **asteroid belt**.

There are a number of phrases that people use to remember the order of the planets. You could try making up your own.

Mercury has the shortest orbit time of all the planets. It takes just 88 days to travel once around the Sun.

The outer planets, in order from the Sun, are:

- **Jupiter** – the largest planet in the solar system. It has a spectacular appearance, with a swirling atmosphere and its Great Red Spot. It also has 16 moons in orbit around it.
- **Saturn**, the sixth planet, is a very bright yellow object in the sky. It has more than 100 000 rings made up of dust, ice and rock. As well as its rings, Saturn has more than 20 satellites in orbit around it.
- **Uranus** also has rings and a total of 15 satellites, five of which are large moons.
- **Neptune**, the eighth planet, is very similar in size and composition to Uranus. Being further away from the Sun, Neptune takes twice as long as Uranus to complete an orbit.

Until 2006 Pluto was regarded as the ninth planet. Then scientists devised a new definition of a planet. According to the new definition, a planet is an object that orbits the Sun and is large enough to have become round due to the force of its own gravity. In addition, a planet has to dominate the neighbourhood around its orbit.

The scale of the Solar System is vast and it is very difficult to fit the Sun and planets on the same diagram. This diagram gives an idea of the relative sizes and distances of the planets from the Sun.

Figure 5.14 Relative sizes and distances of the planets from the Sun

How Science Works

Most people believed that the Earth was flat until about 6000 years ago. Then the Ancient Greek scientists and philosophers proposed the idea that the Earth was a sphere. Aristotle was one of the first thinkers to provide evidence of a spherical Earth in 330BCE. By the early Middle Ages it was widespread knowledge throughout Europe that the Earth was a sphere. However some people, despite the evidence, still believe the world is flat. The **Flat Earth Society** is an organization that seeks to further the belief that the Earth is flat rather than a sphere.

Progress Check

1 List the four inner planets and the four outer planets.
2 How does the time a planet takes to orbit the Earth depend upon the distance from the Sun?

1. Inner: Mercury, Venus, Earth and Mars; Outer: Jupiter, Saturn, Uranus, Neptune
2. The further the distance from the Sun, the longer the time for one orbit.

5.3 How the environment changes

<table>
<tr><td>Learning Summary</td><td>After studying this section you should be able to:
<ul>
<li>describe some of the consequences of acid rain</li>
<li>identify why it is important to monitor air and water pollution</li>
<li>describe a variety of environmental issues</li>
</ul></td></tr>
</table>

Introduction

Some environmental changes occur because of natural processes. For example, mechanical weathering (page 120) occurs because of repeated heating and cooling of rocks. Earthquakes, volcanoes, etc. bring about changes to the environment.

Other processes occur because of human activity. This becomes more serious as the population increases and if people do not think about the damage they are causing. In this topic we are going to consider changes caused by human activity and natural processes.

Acid rain

The pH value of rain water is about 5.5

Rain water is naturally slightly acidic because carbon dioxide dissolves in water forming carbonic acid.

water + carbon dioxide ⟶ carbonic acid

However, the burning of **fossil fuels**, such as coal, produces sulfur dioxide. This dissolves in water forming sulfuric acid.

Vehicle exhausts produce oxides of nitrogen (sometimes written as NO_x). These dissolve in water to form nitric acid.

What are the consequences of acid rain? They include:

1. Damage to stonework on buildings. St Paul's cathedral and Westminster Abbey are just two buildings that show damage due to acid rain. A black skin first appears on the stone. This then blisters and cracks, causing the stone to be seriously disfigured.
2. Rivers and lakes can become more acidic. This kills wildlife including fish and otters. There are many lakes in Norway or Sweden that now have no life.
3. Forests are seriously damaged. Forests in Scandinavia and Germany especially are being damaged by acid rain. Trees are stunted, needles and leaves drop off and the trees die. It has been estimated that acid rain is costing the German forestry industry about £250 million each year.

④ Human life can be affected. Acid conditions can alter levels of copper, lead and aluminium in the body. These changes have been linked with diarrhoea in small babies and breathing disorders.

⑤ Damage to metalwork. Acid rain can speed up corrosion of metals. Wrought iron railings in city areas can show considerable damage.

Monitoring air and water pollution

Monitoring levels of pollution in air and water is important in detecting changes in pollutants over a period of time. In Great Britain about 50 years ago levels of air pollutants were much higher than they are today. In cities there were frequent serious fogs produced by soot ash and tar from the burning of coal in houses and factories. This fog was nicknamed smog and caused 4000 extra deaths in one winter alone in Great Britain.

The Clean Air Act (1956) set up clean air zones where coal could not be burned, only 'smokeless fuels'. As a result of this act and the careful monitoring of air pollution the situation in cities has improved.

> There are websites where you can get data about air pollution.

> In Santiago, Chile, pollution caused by motor vehicles is controlled day to day by monitoring the levels of pollution and then banning vehicles with certain digits in their number plates for the next day.

Figure 5.15 Air pollution in Santiago

iStockphoto / Thinkstock

How Science Works

Nitrogen oxides and unburnt fuel combine in sunlight to produce secondary pollutants including low level ozone. This is called **photochemical smog** and affects people with breathing problems.

Monitoring levels of air pollutants can help planning for a healthier future in our cities.

Global warming

You have probably heard stories about the Earth warming up and some of the effects this might have. This is called **global warming** and is caused by the **greenhouse effect**.

A greenhouse keeps plants warm. Short wavelength light energy from the Sun enters through the glass and warms up the inside of the greenhouse.

Figure 5.16 The greenhouse effect

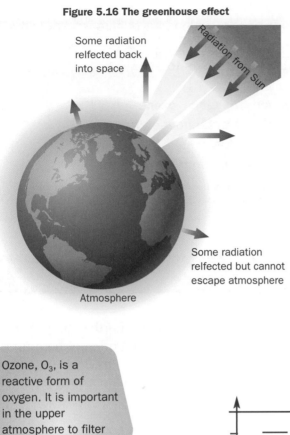

Some radiation reflected back into space

Radiation from Sun

Some radiation reflected but cannot escape atmosphere

Atmosphere

The objects in the greenhouse radiate long wavelength infrared radiation, but this radiation cannot escape back out through the glass. This causes the temperature to rise.

The Earth acts in a similar way but, instead of glass, there are gases in the atmosphere (e.g. carbon dioxide and methane) that do the same job. They let the short wavelength energy in but do not let the long wavelength energy escape. Without the greenhouse effect the surface of the Earth would be too cold for life to exist. The problem of global warming comes about because the concentrations of carbon dioxide, in particular, are rising and the effect is getting greater and surface temperatures are rising.

Figure 5.17 shows a graph of changes in average carbon dioxide concentration and average temperature over the past 200 years.

> Ozone, O_3, is a reactive form of oxygen. It is important in the upper atmosphere to filter out harmful ultraviolet rays. Close to the Earth, however, it is a harmful pollutant.

Figure 5.17 The greenhouse effect

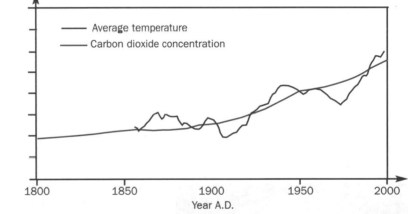

— Average temperature
— Carbon dioxide concentration

Temperature (°C)

1800   1850   1900   1950   2000

Year A.D.

How Science Works

If you look at Figure 5.17 you will see that the concentration of carbon dioxide has increased and the rate of increase (the steepness of the graph) is increasing. You will also see that the average temperature is increasing, but the trend is less regular. These results, and similar ones, have led scientists to link increasing temperature of the Earth with increased carbon dioxide concentrations.

> Don't confuse the greenhouse effect with the destruction of the ozone layer.

Possible effects of global warming are:
- rising temperatures on the Earth's surface
- melting of glaciers and ice caps leading to rising sea levels
- rising ocean temperatures may affect plankton growth
- changes of climate in different parts of the world

Depletion of the ozone layer

There is a layer of ozone, O_3, in the upper part of the Earth's atmosphere called the **stratosphere**. This layer prevents the penetration of harmful UV light from the Sun from reaching the Earth's surface. Ultraviolet radiation affects us causing skin burns, cataracts and skin cancer. It also affects other living organisms.

About 50 years ago an independent scientist, James Lovelock, was making observations of the atmosphere and scientists realised that there were appreciable quantities of chemicals called **CFCs** (chlorofluorocarbons) in the atmosphere. CFCs were chemicals that had been discovered about 50 years before and were used widely in refrigeration and aerosol cans. CFCs were unreactive and all scientists thought they were safe to use.

Figure 5.18 Ozone holes

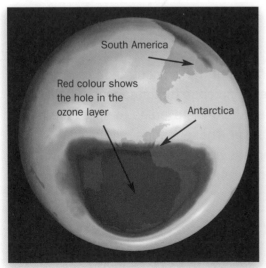

South America

Red colour shows the hole in the ozone layer

Antarctica

In 1985 British scientists, Joseph Farman, Brian Gardiner and Jonathan Shanklin of the British Antarctic Survey, discovered there were areas over the South Pole where the ozone had been largely destroyed. These areas were called **ozone holes**.

Scientists then tried to explain why the ozone was being destroyed, especially over the Poles. Scientists Molina and Rowland proposed that when CFCs break up they form very reactive chlorine radicals, which form a 'chain reaction' that can destroy the ozone. This problem is made worse by the fact that a small amount of CFCs in the upper atmosphere continues to act on ozone molecules for a long while.

Now safer alternatives have been found and most people do not use CFCs and other ozone-depleting compounds.

Governments and scientists from all over the world produced the **Montreal Protocol**, which was a timetable for stopping the use of CFCs and replacing them with safer compounds.

The hope is that the holes in the ozone layer will repair themselves over the next 50 years. For this to happen, all countries have got to stop using harmful CFCs and use the alternatives.

| **How Science Works** | James Lovelock was an independent scientist. He did not work for a company. He was able, therefore, to engage in experimental work that had no immediate economic benefit to a company. Because he was not funded by any company he could make his research impartial. We, therefore, think that his research is reliable. |

| **Progress Check** | 1 Why do you think that the reactions using up ozone work best at cold temperatures?
2 There has been a slight reduction in the size of the ozone holes since the introduction of the Montreal Protocol. Can we be certain that the problem has been solved? |

1. The fact that the holes form over the poles where it is coldest.
2. A slight reduction may be explained by other factors, e.g. a large volcanic eruption. The reduction would have to be observed over a much longer period.

Volcanoes and earthquakes

Volcanic eruptions and earthquakes are natural events that would take place whether or not humans were on the Earth.

Molten rock (called lava), hot gases (including sulfur dioxide) and ash are expelled from inside the volcano. A volcanic eruption can be very dramatic and can have a large effect on the surrounding area. The dust can block out sunlight and the gases can contribute to acid rain and global warming.

Figure 5.19 shows an explosive eruption of a volcano.

Figure 5.19

Hemera / Thinkstock

Figure 5.20 The structure of a volcano

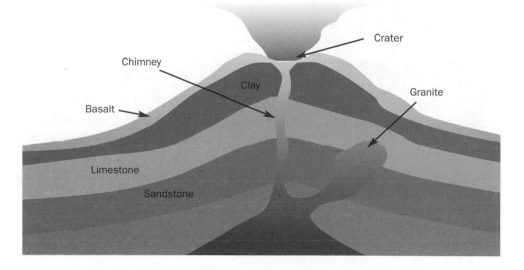

Crater

Chimney

Clay

Granite

Basalt

Limestone

Sandstone

Figure 5.20 shows a cross-section diagram through a volcano. It shows how rocks from inside the Earth escape through the chimney of the volcano. If these molten rocks crystallize...

- inside the volcano they can produce a rock called **granite**
- on the surface they form a rock called **basalt**.

Not all volcanoes are spectacular. Volcanoes that erupt regularly are called **active volcanoes**. Ones that might react at some time are called **dormant volcanoes** and ones that will not erupt in the future are called **extinct volcanoes**.

The Earth's outer crust is made up from a series of very large **tectonic plates** that can move very slowly. Figure 5.21 shows the plates and their direction of movement. The red spots show where earthquakes occur. You will notice that many of these occur at plate boundaries where plates rub against each other.

When an earthquake occurs under the oceans it can produce a huge tidal wave called a **tsunami**.

Figure 5.21

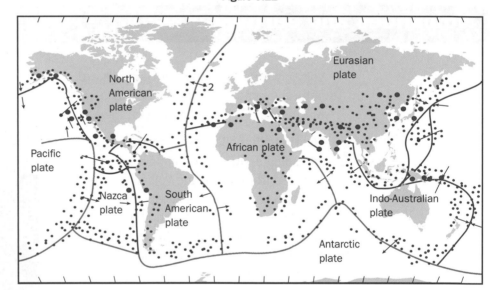

How Science Works	The ideas of plate tectonics were developed in 1912 by the German scientist Alfred Wegener. At first Wegener's theories were disputed by other scientists and it wasn't until about 1960 that scientists realized that Wegener was correct because his theories explained scientific phenomena.

Progress Check	1 What is the usual cause of an earthquake? 2 Some rock that is formed when lava from a volcano solidifies contains bubbles. Suggest why these bubbles form. 3 Suggest why crystals of basalt are smaller than crystals of granite.

1. Tectonic plates rubbing together. 2. Volcanic gases are trapped in the rock as it crystallizes.
3. Crystallisation occurs more slowly inside the Earth than on the Earth's surface.

Assessment questions

1. Use words from the list to answer the questions that follow.

   Earth   Mercury   Moon   Neptune   Pluto   Sun

   (a) Which body gives out light? _____ **[1]**

   (b) Which object orbits the Earth? _____ **[1]**

   (c) Which object is closest to the Sun? _____ **[1]**

   (d) Which object did scientists think was a planet until 2006? _____ **[1]**

   (e) Write down the names of three planets in order of distance from the Sun. Put the one closest to the Sun first.

   _____ **[2]**

2. What type of force acts between the Earth and the Moon? Choose from the following list.

   electrical   frictional   gravitational   magnetic

   _____ **[1]**

3. The diagrams show the surfaces of two rocks A and B.

   (a) Describe the shape of the grains that make up rock A.

   _____
   _____ **[1]**

   (b) Suggest how the grains in rock B became rounded in shape.

   _____
   _____
   _____ **[2]**

   (c) Why can rock B soak up more water than rock A?

   _____
   _____ **[1]**

Assessment questions

4. Kim looks carefully at two rock samples labelled A and B. She writes her observations in a table.

	Rock A	Rock B
Colour	Some white crystals and some shiny black ones	White crystals with some brown veins running through it
Size of crystals	Large	Small

(a) Why does she think that neither of these rocks is sedimentary?

_____ [1]

(b) What evidence is there in the table to suggest that Rock A is made up of more than one mineral?

_____ [1]

(c) What evidence is there to suggest that Rock A was crystallised slowly?

_____ [1]

(d) Rock B is a metamorphic rock formed from a sedimentary rock. What conditions are needed to turn a sedimentary rock into a metamorphic rock?

_____ [2]

5. The diagram represents the Sun and the three planets closest to the Sun.

Sun   V   M   Earth

(a) Write down the names of the planets labelled M and V.

_____ [2]

(b) Which object shown on the diagram is a light source?

_____ [1]

(c) Venus can be seen from the Earth as a very bright object in the night sky. Explain why Venus looks to be brighter than the other planets.

_____

_____

_____ [2]

(d) On the diagram, shade the part of the Earth that is in darkness.

_____ [1]

(e) Explain how the movement of the Earth causes day and night.

_____ [1]

Assessment questions

6. Methane, like carbon dioxide, is a greenhouse gas but its effects are more damaging.

There are huge amounts of methane trapped in ice crystals in the North Polar Ice cap. This is called methane hydrate. If this ice was to melt, methane gas would be released into the atmosphere.

(a) What might cause this ice cap to melt?

_____

_____ **[1]**

(b) What problems would the melting of the ice cap cause?

_____

_____

_____

_____

_____ **[3]**

(c) (i) Some scientists suggest that it might be possible to extract methane from the methane hydrate and use it as a fuel. Outline how this could be done.

_____

_____

_____ **[2]**

(ii) Why might this approach not be an advantage?

_____

_____

_____

_____

_____ **[3]**

Assessment questions

7. Granite and basalt are two igneous rocks. Granite is formed inside the Earth and is made up of large crystals. Basalt is found on the surface of the Earth and is made up of small crystals.

    (a) Explain why the crystal size of the two rocks is different.

    _____

    _____

    _____ **[2]**

    (b) If granite is formed inside the Earth how can it be found on the surface of the Earth?

    _____ **[1]**

    (c) Describe the processes by which igneous rocks such as granite and basalt can be converted into sedimentary rocks and then into metamorphic rocks.

    _____

    _____

    _____

    _____

    _____

    _____

    _____

    _____ **[5]**

Assessment answers

Chapter One
Pages 22–26

Levels 3–4

1. Increases **[1]** or doubles **[2]**
   Tip: The first response is correct, but is not the best answer.
2. **(a)** A is damp but B is dry   **[1]**
   (b) Aphids   **[1]**
   (c)

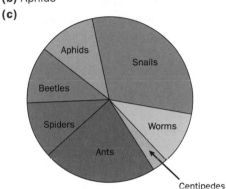

   Correct segments [1] Correct labelling [1]
   (d) Centipedes **[1]** There are fewer centipedes so they are likely to be further up the food chain **[1]**

Levels 5–6

3. **(a)** Continuous, as there are no distinct groups   **[1]**
   (b)

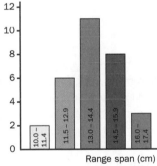

   Only allow 1 mark for a single error   **[2]**
   (c) The chart shows the greatest number have the span in the middle **[1]** with the numbers decreasing as the span gets shorter **[1]** or longer **[1]**
   (d) Any three from: The sample of 30 is too small to be reliable **[1]**; A much larger sample would be needed **[1]**; No distinction between boys and girls **[1]**; No age quoted **[1]**
4. **(a)** The germinating peas produce a change in temperature; It is an increase in temperature   **[2]**
   (b) To ensure there is no increase in temperature even if the peas were not germinating   **[1]**

Levels 7–8

5. While this is true for up to 20 cigarettes a day **[1]**, it is not true above 20 cigarettes a day **[1]**. Increasing the number of cigarettes does not have much effect. **[1]**
6. **(a) (i)** 0.80g
   (ii) 1.00g
   (iii) 0.90g
   (iv) 1.40g
   All four correct [1]
   (b)

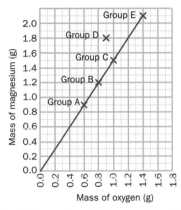

   Suitable scales [1] Correct plotting [1] Correct line [1]
   (c) Group D **[1]**. Smaller mass of magnesium oxide or oxygen than expected **[1]**. Not all the magnesium had burned **[1]**.
   (d) If no magnesium is burned then no oxygen is combined   **[1]**
   (e) We would expect mass of oxygen to be zero when mass of magnesium is 0g   **[1]**

Chapter Two
Pages 58–61

Levels 3–4

1. **(a)** Plant plankton   **[1]**
   Tip: This question occurs often. Remember, the producer in a food chain or web is the plant.
   (b) Four   **[1]**
   (c) One   **[1]**
   (d) The numbers all decrease **[1]** because their food supply has been destroyed **[1]**.
   Tip: Questions often ask about how the changing numbers of one species affect the other species. An increased food supply leads to an increase in numbers of organism further up the food chain.
2. **(a)** testicle   **[1]**
   (b) cervix   **[1]**
   (c) ovary   **[1]**
   (d) fallopian tubes   **[1]**
   (e) uterus   **[1]**

Assessment answers

3. (a) **Advantages:** New plants will all be identical in colour and form; It's quicker than growing new plants from seed; Cheaper **[2]**

   Disadvantages: Any diseases in the old plants will be present in the new; There is no chance of producing new colours **[2]**

   Tip: You must give two advantages and two disadvantages

   (b) (i) There are no chloroplasts in the yellow parts of the leaf. **[1]** Chlorophyll in chloroplasts is needed for photosynthesis. **[1]**

   (ii) carbon dioxide + water **[1]** ➜ glucose (or starch or sugar) + oxygen **[1]**

4. (a) The cell has chloroplasts **[1]** and a cell wall **[1]**.

   Tip: These are the key differences between animal and plant cells. Remember, not all plant cells have chloroplasts – only those in the green parts of the plant.

   (b) (i) The nucleus **[1]**

   (ii) The cell wall **[1]**

   (iii) The chloroplasts **[1]**

   (c) (i) The root **[1]**

   (ii) It has a large surface area to absorb water from the soil **[1]**

   Tip: This question is testing whether you can identify ways in which cells are adapted to do their job.

5. Selective breeding **[1]**; High yields are obtained by choosing desirable cows and bulls for breeding **[1]**; Repeated over many generations **[1]**; Improved diet **[1]**

6. (a) $6CO_2 + 6H_2O \longrightarrow C_6H_{12}O_6 + 6O_2$

   One mark for products and one mark for balancing equation

   (b) Oxygen diffuses into the air **[1]** through the stomata in the leaves **[1]**

   (c) (i) Light intensity **[1]**

   (ii) Increased concentration of carbon dioxide in the atmosphere in the greenhouse. **[1]**

Chapter Three
Pages 76–79

1. (a) Silver colour **[1]**; Conductor of electricity **[1]**

   (b) Paraffin wax melts over a range of temperatures **[1]**; Pure substances melt at a sharp temperature **[1]**

   (c) (i) Compound **[1]**

   (ii) Mercury oxide **[1]**

2. Add bicarbonate of soda and wash with water **[1]**

3. Metals – B, D and E **[1]**
   Non-metals – A and C **[1]**

4. **True:** A, B and C; **False:** D and E.
   All 5 correct [3], 4 correct [2], 3 correct [1]

5. (a) There is a decrease in mass when zinc carbonate is heated **[1]**; No change in mass when zinc oxide is heated **[1]**

   (b) zinc oxide **[1]** + carbon dioxide **[1]**

   Tip: The information in the table should suggest that when zinc carbonate is heated zinc oxide is formed.

6. (a) 4 **[1]**

   (b) Na – 1, H – 1, C – 1, O – 3 **[1]**

   (c) 6 **[1]**

7. **Accept any six points from:**

   During first six minutes liquid is cooling **[1]**

   Particles are irregularly arranged and moving slower as temperature falls **[1]**

   At 78° the temperature remains constant for about 4 minutes **[1]**

   Liquid solidifying **[1]**

   Particles become regularly arranged **[1]**

   After 10 minutes solid is cooling **[1]**

   Vibration of particles is reducing **[1]**

Chapter Four
Pages 115–118

1. (a) **Accept any two from:** oil, gas, coal. **1 mark each.**

   Tip: Remember, a non-renewable source will run out within the lifetime of the Earth and cannot be replaced.

   (b) **Accept any two from:** wind, waves, tides, geothermal, solar. **1 mark each.**

   (c) (i) On; Off; On **1 mark each.** **[3]**

   (ii) Move switch A from up to down **[1]**
   Move switch B from down to up **[1]**

   (iii) For switching a light on or off at either of two switches **[1]**

   Tip: This type of circuit is called a two-way switching circuit. It is commonly used for switching a landing light either upstairs or downstairs.

2. (a) D **[1]**

   (b) A book scatters light or reflects it in all directions **[1]**

   (c) (i) E **[1]**

   (ii) They are both upright **[1]**; They are the same size **[1]**

3. (a) 30m/s × 2.0s **[1]** = 60m **[1]**

Tip: You need to have the correct unit to gain the 2nd mark.

(b) 4.0s **[1]**

Tip: This is testing your skills at reading data from a graph. A common error is to answer '6 seconds', ignoring the 2.0 seconds before the car started braking.

(c) Distance = speed × time = 15m/s × 4.0s **[1]**

= 60m **[1]**

(d) 120m **[1]**

Tip: The total stopping distance is the 'thinking distance' plus the 'braking distance'

4. (a) Area = $\frac{Force}{Pressure}$ **[1]**

= $\frac{600N}{1\,200\,000Pa}$ **[1]**

= 0.0005m^2 **[unit must be correct]** **[1]**

(b) Pressure doubles / 2 400 000Pa **[1]**

5. (a) D **[1]**

(b) (i) Doubling the voltage from 0.5V to 1.0V doubles the current from 0.1A to 0.2A **[1]**

However, doubling the voltage from 1.0V to 2.0V increases the current from 0.25A to 0.35A **[1]**

This is not double and so not always true **[1]**

(ii) The increased current means a greater movement of charged particles in the circuit. **[1]** The moving charged particles have more energy to transfer to the lamp **[1]**

Chapter Five
Pages 135–138

1. (a) Sun **[1]**

(b) Moon **[1]**

(c) Mercury **[1]**

(d) Pluto **[1]**

(e) Mercury, Earth, Neptune **[All three plants correct 1 mark; Planets in correct order 1 mark]**

2. Gravitational **[1]**

3. (a) Interlocking crystals **[1]**

(b) Pieces of rock rub together **[1]** as they travel along a river **[1]**

(c) Water can fit in the spaces between the grains in rock B.

4. (a) They both contain crystals **[1]**

(b) It contains two types of crystals, white and black mixed together **[1]**

(c) Rock A forms large crystals, which are formed when the magma crystallizes slowly. **[1]**

(d) High pressure and high temperature **[2]**

Tip: Two conditions are needed for two marks. You are not expected to give actual temperature and pressures.

5. (a) M is Mercury **[1]**

V is Venus **[1]**

(b) The Sun. **[1]**

Tip: Suns are stars that give out light because they are very hot. Planets and moons are seen by the light that they reflect.

(c) Venus is close to the Sun, so it is illuminated brightly. **[1]**

Venus is close to the Earth, so the light it reflects has spread out less than that of other planets when it reaches the Earth. **[1]**

(d) The side of the Earth facing away from the Sun should be shaded **[1]**

(e) The Earth spins on its axis. **[1]**

Tip: The Earth rotates on its axis once every day. Take care not to confuse this with the Earth's movement around the Sun. One complete orbit around the Sun takes one year.

6. (a) A rise in the Earth's temperature **[1]**

(b) Methane released into the atmosphere **[1]**

Infrared radiation from the Earth is blocked **[1]**

Causes Earth's temperature to rise, which leads to more methane being released **[1]**

(c) (i) Transport methane hydrate in a refrigerated tanker **[1]** to power station where it could be melted and used as a fuel **[1]**

(ii) Burning methane produces more carbon dioxide **[1]**, which is a greenhouse gas causing the Earth's temperature to rise **[1]**. This releases more methane into the atmosphere **[1]**

7. (a) Crystallisation occurs quickly on the surface, producing small crystals **[1]**

Crystallisation occurs slowly inside the Earth, producing larger crystals **[1]**

(b) Erosion of the rocks above the granite **[1]**

(c) Igneous rocks are broken down by weathering / erosion to produce sediments **[1]**

Sediments are transported in rivers, etc. **[1]**

Deposited and compressed to form sedimentary rocks **[1]**

Sedimentary rocks converted into metamorphic rocks by high temperature **[1]** and high pressure **[1]**

Science word list

To be successful at KS3 you need to learn the language of Science and to be able to use this language correctly. The following words are important and you should be sure that you know exactly what they mean. Some words (shown with *) can have more than one meaning.

Chapter 1

apparatus	hazard	precision	trend
bar chart	hypothesis	prediction	variable
evaluation	investigation	risk	
fair test	line graph	theory	

Chapter 2

adolescence	diet	mineral	root hair
alveolus (plural alveoli)	embryo	mutation	scrotum
amphibian	emphysema	nucleus (plural nuclei)*	selective breeding
antibiotic	environment	organ	sexual reproduction
anus	epidermis	ovary	skeleton
asexual reproduction	ethology	ovum (plural ova)	species
bacterium (plural bacteria)	fat	palisade cell	sperm
	fertilisation	penis	stem cell
bronchiole	fibre	period*	stomata (plural stoma)
bronchus	foetus (or fetus)	photosynthesis	testes
capillary	food chain	placenta	thorax
carbohydrate	food web	predator	toxin
carnivore	gene	pregnancy	trachea
cell*	habitat	prey	umbilical cord
cell membrane	herbivore	producer	vacuole
chlorophyll	immune	protein	variation
chloroplast	imprinting	psychology	vertebrate
cilia	instinct	reflex	virus
conditioning	invertebrate	reptile	vitamin
cuticle	lung	respiration	vulva
cytoplasm	mammal	respiratory system	zygote
diaphragm	menstrual cycle	rib	

Chapter 3

acid
atom
base
chemical change
chromatography
combustion
compound
diffusion
dissolve
distillation

ductile
element
evaporation
formula
fuel
gas
group
hazard sign
indicator
insoluble

liquid
malleable
metal
metalloid
mixture
molecule
neutral
non-metal
oxide
period*

Periodic Table
pH value
saturated solution
solid
soluble
solution
symbol
Universal Indicator

Chapter 4

air resistance
ammeter
ampere
amplitude
balanced forces
conductor
current
ear drum
electricity
electrolysis
energy
force
frequency
friction
fuel cell

generator
geothermal energy
gradient
gravitational potential
        energy
hertz
image
infra-red
insulator
joule
kinetic energy
luminous
magnetic field
mass
moment

Newton
non-luminous
oscilloscope
ossicles
pascal
pitch
pivot
pressure
real image
reflection
refraction
renewable resource
resistance
resistive forces
scatter

solar cell
sound
speed
turbine
ultra-violet
unbalanced forces
variable resistor
vacuum
velocity
vibrate
virtual image
voltage
volt
voltmeter
weight

Chapter 5

acid rain
asteroid
conglomerate
constellation
crystals
erosion
fossil fuel
fossils

global warming
grains
greenhouse effect
igneous
impermeable
lava
metamorphic
minerals

ozone holes
ozone layer
permeable
planet
rock cycle
satellite
sediment
sedimentary

Solar System
star
stratosphere
tectonic plates
tsunami
volcano
weathering

Index